BEHOLD THE
BUILDER

SCIENTIFIC EVIDENCES FOR THE BIBLICAL GOD

ERIC PARKER

ONESTONE
BIBLICAL RESOURCES

Interior figures herein have been used by permission.
For a listing of credits, please see pages171-176, which constitute a
continuation of this copyright page.

Design, informational graphics and illustrations
by Stephen Sebree / Moonlight Graphic Works

Published by One Stone Press
979 Lovers Lane
Bowling Green, KY 42103

Printed in the United States of America

ISBN: 978-1-941422-47-2

ONESTONE
BIBLICAL RESOURCES

Dedication

This book is dedicated to the mothers in my life.

Firstly, to my beloved. You are the love of my life. I cannot fathom a life without you and our children in it. You are incredible. I thank God for you.

Secondly, to my mom. I am who I am because of values you instilled in me from the start. I thank God for you.

Thirdly, to my mother-in-law. You have been a constant source of encouragement to me. I thank God for you.

Fourthly, to the 100s of mothers I have in the kingdom (Matthew 19:29; Mark 3:33-35). Your constant encouragement has empowered me in good times and in bad. I thank God for you.

Table of Contents

Acknowledgements **6**

Preface **7**

Chapter 1 The War Between Science and Faith **9**

Chapter 2 God, Science, And Origins **19**

Chapter 3 The Age of the Earth **33**

Chapter 4 Dinosaurs: Friend Or Foe for Christians? **45**

Chapter 5 What Geology And the Fossil Record Do NOT Show **61**

Chapter 6 What Geology And the Fossil Record Do Show **77**

Chapter 7 An Introduction to Intelligent Design **91**

Chapter 8 Anthropic Constants **103**

Chapter 9 The Designed Man **113**

Chapter 10 Information **129**

Chapter 11 Miscellaneous Biological Marvels **143**

Chapter 12 An Uphill Battle **159**

Acknowledgements

Writing a book, especially one's first, especially in such an area of study, requires support. In addition to those sources of helpful information included in the footnote citation and to those pillars of encouragement mentioned in the dedication, there are a couple persons I would like to give a special acknowledgment to at this juncture.

To my editor, Andrew Yeater, I am indebted to your professional and academic skills. Writing is a technical venture, and, to do it well, guidelines are helpful. Thank you for your red pen, for your suggestions, and for your friendship. Who knew in our college years that we would work together on such a project as this?

To my designer, Steve Sebree of Moonlight Graphic Works, I am also indebted to you for your professional assistance. You put a great deal of effort into this to make it readable and aesthetically pleasing. You helped me immensely with the graphics and layout, two areas in particular in which I would have been severely limited. I am especially thankful to you and my father-in-law, Fred Echols, for being the ones who suggested the sermon series in the first place, the two of you being the elders at the Taylorsville Road church of Christ in Louisville, Kentucky. You both encouraged me throughout the production of those sermons.

To my family, friends, and those who gave me such great feedback on the initial sermons and motivated me to write this work, I applaud you for your support. May others benefit from your friendship and love as I have.

Preface

In the spring of 2018, the elders at the Taylorsville Road church of Christ in Louisville, Kentucky requested that I speak on the relationship between science and faith. They did this because they knew it was an obstacle for many in general and even some specifically among our group. As is usually the case, when one sermon is asked for, the preacher (me in this case) finds a way to expand that into a series of lessons!

It became readily apparent that much research would be involved in such a process. I am formally educated, but limited only to the level of undergraduate work (Perhaps that will change when, Lord willing, my children grow and mature, opening my schedule more!). For that reason, I voraciously read as much as I could, attempting to sift between scientific fact and fiction. I read small volumes and large volumes. I watched documentaries, interviews, and academic discourses. I also searched high and low online for resources that would benefit this search. I put hundreds of hours into the lessons.

My heart and mind were set on providing a system of strong, sound, and rational argumentation demonstrating that Christians are not scientifically illiterate and unread, nor is the Bible antiquated and obsolete. I presented my findings in the form of nine sermons over the course of several months. The series was well received and faith grew exponentially as Christians and non-Christians who heard the lessons began to see that what we see in the world agrees with what we see in God's Word. God's general revelation in nature matched perfectly to His specific revelation in Scripture.

Several commented that the research I put into these lessons would serve well as a book. Initially reluctant because of the innumerable books found in libraries both physical and electronic (cf. Eccl 12:12), I agreed after the encouragement and instigation of loved ones. This book is the product of many hours of research, but it is certainly not the best. There are other books that are more professionally written, better researched, more technical, and more exhaustive. The intent here was to create an intermediate work—not too long and not too short, not overly difficult and not overly simplistic. Perhaps the intended structure of this book will also speak in a way that will remain with you in ways that others do not. There is an old Russian saying that speaks to this: *"The effect of words can last one hour, but a book serves as a perpetual reminder."* I truly and humbly hope this book will serve you well in this regard. Please note also that this book specifically focuses on scientific evidences and apologetics. Matters of historical and philosophical apologetics are, for the most part, not directly engaged in with this work, although undertones will be present. The possibility of miracles, the problem of evil, the historical witness to the resurrection of Jesus, and other discussions are certainly helpful and important, even crucial, but they are not in the direct purview of this book.

With the relentless intellectual onslaught against Christians in this break-neck-paced world, I sincerely hope this book will enlighten you to the theological benefits of scientific study. Please keep in mind, however, that scientific inquiry possesses no inherent faith value unless the Word of God speaks to it first (cf. Rom 10:17). For this reason, the book will regularly return to the Scriptures to root the discussion in the Word of God. May you choose to passionately love the Lord your God with all of your heart, soul, mind, and strength and may your defense of God and Christianity be sharpened by this resource. If that happens, then this book will have served its purpose. To God be the glory!

CHAPTER 1

The War Between Science and Faith

In the second-to-last book in the Bible, the younger brother of Jesus of Nazareth passionately writes to His first century disciples,

> *Beloved, while I was making every effort to write you about our common salvation, I felt the necessity to write to you appealing that you contend earnestly for the faith which was once for all handed down to the saints* (Jude 3).

Peter, the Apostle of Jesus, similarly writes,

> *but sanctify Christ as Lord in your hearts, always being ready to make a defense to everyone who asks you to give an account for the hope that is in you, yet with gentleness and reverence* (1 Pet 3:15).

Christians are commended and commanded to contend earnestly for the faith. Different elements of this defensive and offensive campaign require different strategies. In view of this, Christian apologetics requires constant methodological updating. While endless books have been written defending Christianity, there is still a consistent need for more publishing. The Enemy is persistent, more persistent than he is often given credit: *"Be of sober spirit, be on the alert. Your adversary, the devil, prowls around like a roaring lion, seeking someone to devour. But resist him, firm in your faith"* (1 Pet 5:8-9). His persistence is often veiled because he shrouds himself in a deceptive cloak, a method which Paul of Tarsus exposes in 2 Cor 11:12-15:

> *But what I am doing I will continue to do, so that I may cut off opportunity from those who desire an opportunity to be regarded just as we are in the matter about which they are boasting. For such men are false apostles, deceitful workers, disguising themselves as apostles of Christ. No wonder, for even Satan disguises himself as an angel of light. Therefore it is not surprising if his servants also disguise themselves as servants of righteousness, whose end will be according to their deeds.*

No doubt these truths are telling. But, why this book in particular?

Browbeating

Christians have been ostracized, mischaracterized, and ridiculed for years as being un-informed, un-thinking, and unwitting.[1] This is particularly true during the post-Enlightenment period. Modernism and Post-modernism have taken center stage, dethroning theistic thinking with atheistic intellectual bravado. Science, in particular, has been crudely and incorrectly re-defined in terms of exclusively natural processes, and a hedge against supernatural involvement has been erected in the spirit of Babel's Tower.

Figure 1.1 Inherit the Wind

As a result, all intellectual discussions quickly devolve into worldview discussions, namely the alleged superiority and intellectual prowess of atheistic naturalism.[2] Recognition that these discussions have left the original subject matter and entered this plane is totally absent on the part of many naturalists. Rather, under the shroud of "science," Christians have been regarded as bumbling morons who are intellectually inept, irrational, and indisposed to accept the truth of scientific reason. Timothy Keller comments on this in his *New York Times* Bestseller, *The Reason for God,*

> *The bestselling books by Richard Dawkins, Daniel C. Dennett, and Sam Harris assume that science in general, and evolutionary science in particular, has made belief in God unnecessary and obsolete. Dawkins said very famously that 'although atheism might have been logically tenable before Darwin, Darwin made it possible to be an intellectually fulfilled atheist.' In* The God Delusion *he goes much further. He argues that you cannot be an intelligent scientific thinker and still hold religious beliefs. It is one or the other . . . the more intelligent, rational, and scientifically minded you are, the less you will be able to believe in God.*[3]

---

[1] A perfect illustration of this is the media's completely erroneous portrayal of the Scopes Trial itself (e.g. *Inherit The Wind*) and even the vitriol against those who took the creation viewpoint in that particular case. A classic example is H.L. Mencken's obituary for William Jennings Bryan, the prosecutor for the trial, who writes, *"Bryan was deluded by a childish theology full of almost pathological hatred of all learning, all human dignity, all beauty, all fine and noble things. Imagine a gentleman, and you have imagined everything he was not."* Let it be noted that Bryan died five days after the trial so Mencken's comments were fresh off the trial.

[2] By atheistic naturalism, we mean the prior dismissal of God as a foundational matter of worldview with the effect that the researcher is restricted to an exclusively naturalistic cause for the universe. We will use this term synonymously with methodological naturalism.

As the Apostle Peter warns,

> *You therefore, beloved, knowing this beforehand, be on your guard so that you are not carried away by the error of unprincipled men and fall from your own steadfastness, but grow in the grace and knowledge of our Lord and Savior Jesus Christ. To Him be the glory, both now and to the day of eternity. Amen* (2 Pet 3:17-18).

The Christian's View of Reason And Science[4]

Simply put, there is no inherent disagreement between the pursuit to understand the universe (i.e. science) and theology. Plenty of scientists, educated at the most prestigious universities in the world and with swathes of credentials, subscribe to forms of theism, specifically Christianity. Raw intellect and pure reason do not tend to be the issue.

In reality, history attests to the interrelationship between science and religion.[5] During the Middle Ages and leading into the Enlightenment, most major discoveries were made by religious individuals.[6] Yet, as Freud and Thomas Huxley and their ilk decimated religious thought by gutting the belly of the inspiration of God and the common sense belief in God (cf. Rom 1), science primarily became the domain of the atheist.

In truth, Christians have a moral responsibility and divine imperative to use their cognitive faculties to deduce truths

Figure 1.2 In Raphael's "School of Athens," Plato is pointing upwards to the ethereal realm and Aristotle is pointing downward to the corporeal realm illustrating the age-old debate between scientists as to whether or not the supernatural should be included in science.

---

[3] Timothy Keller, *The Reason for God* (New York: Riverhead Books, 2009), 87-88.

[4] Faith and reason are not mutually exclusive but rather mutually compatible. *"Now faith is the substance of things hoped for, the evidence of things not seen"* (Heb 11:1). For a thought provoking presentation on this relationship, consult: Ronald H. Nash, *Faith and Reason: Searching for a Rational Faith* (Grand Rapids: Acad. Books, 1988).

[5] For an analysis of this history of religion on scientific discovery and development, see: Stanley L. Jaki, *Science and Creation: from Eternal Cycles to an Oscillating Universe* (Edinburgh: Scottish Academic Press, 1986).

[6] Examples are endless: Hildegard of Bingen, Robert Grosseteste, Albertus Magnus, Jean Buridan, Nicole Oresme, Nicholas of Cusa, Otto Brunfels, Galileo Galilei, Laurentius Gothus, Blaise Pascal, Robert Boyle, Johannes Keppler, Antoine Lavoisier, Georges Cuvier, et al.

around them. Jesus Himself claimed that the most important commandment of God was to *"Love the Lord your God with all of your mind."* (Matt 22:37). This is lost sometimes because of the placement of "mind" in the order of the verse, which is typically rendered, *"You shall love the Lord your God with all your heart, and with all your soul, and with all your mind."* Despite this common oversight, Christians are properly required to use and develop their faculties.[7]

Oftentimes, the roadblock for many in fulfilling this divine command is fear. Being browbeaten and labeled a certain way tends to have that affect, especially when most educational providers are steeped in methodological naturalism.[8] Even if one does possess the mental equipment necessary to go toe-to-toe, blockades such as tenure, graduation, and social acceptance are indeed formidable. Fear can, to paraphrase John Eldredge, cause Christians to approach apologetics as though they were stepping onto the beaches of Normandy with a lawn chair and a book to read! How pitiful!

On occasion, you will even find some believers arguing that because our reasoning abilities are detrimentally affected by sin—commonly referred to as the noetic effects of sin—that we cannot depend on these faculties. This flimsy excuse holds no water, although attempts at justifying this timid attitude have appealed to 1 Cor 1:21-25, which reads,

> *For since in the wisdom of God the world through its wisdom did not come to know God, God was well-pleased through the foolishness of the message preached to save those who believe. For indeed Jews ask for signs and Greeks search for wisdom; but we preach Christ crucified, to Jews a stumbling block and to Gentiles foolishness, but to those who are the called, both Jews and Greeks, Christ the power of God and the wisdom of God. Because the foolishness of God is wiser than men, and the weakness of God is stronger than men.*

However, to view this passage as forbidding the exercise of reason and logical argumentation is to misunderstand the point and ignore the context. The point being made in this passage is that the medium by which God accomplished redemption—the cross of Jesus Christ—did not make sense to many individuals, both Jew and Gentile, because of presuppositions that forbade that possibility. This passage clearly does not teach that the wisdom of God is found in ignoring our reasoning abilities. Moreover, God Himself calls us to be reasonable—*"Come now, and*

---

[7] The same moral imperative is inherent in the Parable of the Talents (Matt 25:14-30). "Talent" may be viewed as analogous to cognitive capabilities and potential.

[8] John Dewey's signing of the *Humanist Manifesto* is an excellent example of chief influences in our educational system being shaped by destructive philosophies that grow out of methodological naturalism.

let us reason together," says the Lord (Isa 1:18). As the Apostle Paul commends to Timothy, *"For God has not given us a spirit of timidity, but of power and love and discipline"* (2 Tim 1:7).

Origins Science And Operational Science

As reason would have it, Christians should employ science as an asset in the available arsenal to arm our apologetic. Many have availed themselves of this field of knowledge, yet criticisms expectantly arise like tares among wheat. One of the most common critiques of Christian apologists is that the methodology employed to provide a scientific apologetic depends more on philosophical conceptions of history than on "actual" science. While this is true in some cases, typically this critique is a red herring.

While some "actual" science occurs in a laboratory setting with numerous controls that help simulate real life situations and variables, most of science occurs outside the lab. In the real world, science and history are interlaced as tightly as the double helix bond of DNA. As an example, the systematic consideration of origins and past events may not fit into a narrow philosophical definition of observational science, but does fit into the realm of origins/ historical science. This is a form of scientific discovery and study regularly used by theists AND atheists alike, including researchers in paleontology, cosmology, archaeology, etc. In fact, evolution is identified as a form of historical science by one of the twentieth century's most influential evolutionists, Ernst Mayr, who says

Figure 1.3

> *Evolutionary biology, in contrast with physics and chemistry, is an historical science—the evolutionist attempts to explain events and processes that have already taken place. Laws and experiments are inappropriate techniques for the explication of such events and processes. Instead one constructs a historical narrative, consisting of a tentative reconstruction of the particular scenario that led to the events one is trying to explain.*

He proceeded to add, ironically: *"No educated person any longer questions the validity of the so-called theory of evolution, which we know now to be a simple fact."*[9]

---

[9] Ernst Mayr, "Darwin's Influence on Modern Thought," *Scientific American* 283 (2000): 80, 83.

Science Requires Interpretation

Philosopher of science Stephen C. Meyer has done extensive work illustrating that science requires interpretation. In his landmark *New York Times* Best Seller, *Darwin's Doubt*, he details how much interpretation is required in even defining science itself! He spends an entire chapter cataloging the plethora of issues involved. A few rapid-fire quotations from this chapter will suffice:

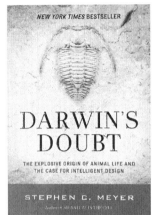

Figure 1.4

Theories that scientists have rejected as false because of their inability to explain or describe the evidence often meet the very criteria or methodological features (testability, falsifiability, repeatability, observability, etc.) that allegedly characterize true science. On the other hand, many highly esteemed or successful theories often lack allegedly necessary features of genuine science

If scientists and philosophers of science do not have an agreed-upon definition of science, how can they settle questions about which theories do and do not qualify as scientific? If scientists lack such a definition, it's difficult to argue that any particular theory is unscientific by nature

Depending upon which criteria are used to adjudicate their scientific status, and provided metaphysically neutral criteria are selected to make such assessments, intelligent design and materialistic origins theories invariably prove equally scientific or unscientific

Any rule that prevents us from considering such an explanation [for the true cause of a human artifact for example, EP] diminishes the rationality of science, because it prevents scientists from considering a possibly—and in this case obviously—true explanation. And the truth matters, not least in science. For this reason, the 'rules of science' should not commit us to rejecting possibly true theories before we even consider the evidence. But that is exactly what methodological naturalism does

In the science world, as in the media, 'creationist' is a dirty word; it's like calling someone a Communist used to be in the 1950s. Such attempts to stigmatize

---

[10] Stephen C. Meyer, *Darwin's Doubt: The Explosive Origin of Animal Life and the Case for Intelligent Design* (New York: HarperOne, 2014), 382-403.

results that challenge a favored theory illustrate how an ideological monopoly in science can stifle inquiry and discussion

Even if all the data point to an intelligent designer, such a hypothesis is [wrongly, EP] *excluded from science because it is not naturalistic.*[10]

Concluding Thought: Missing What Is Right in Front of Us

Materialists, even the highly educated ones, miss what is standing right in front of them because of the application of a set of blinders that often go unacknowledged and unchallenged. G. K. Chesterton, ardent Christian apologist of yesteryear, wrote a short story that illustrated this in 1911. He entitled it "The Invisible Man." In this story, a person is murdered in an apartment whose sole entrance was watched by four trustworthy men who claim that nobody entered or left the building during their watch. A brilliant French detective and his friend, a Catholic priest named Father Brown, investigate the case. Father Brown observes a set of footprints in freshly laid snow and inquires as to what the

Figure 1.5 G.K. Chesterton (1903)

cause of them is. One of the guards cries, "God! An invisible man!" After further inquiry, Father Brown unravels the case. He reveals that one indeed had gone into the apartment but not one of the guards suspected could possibly be the murderer. He calls him, "A mentally invisible man." He then reveals that the murderer was, in fact, the postman, dressed handsomely, even carrying the body in his mailbag right in front of the guards! The guards overlook the obvious explanation because they had dismissed from their minds the possibility of the postman being the murderer.

Figure 1.6

C.S. Lewis makes the same point regarding the stubborn unbelief of Uncle Andrew in his *Chronicles of Narnia* book *The Magician's Nephew*. Lewis writes,

When the great moment came and the Beasts spoke, he missed the whole point, for a rather interesting reason. When the Lion had first begun singing, long ago when it was still quite dark, he had realized that the noise was a song. And he had disliked the song very much. It made him think and feel things he did not want to think and feel. Then, when the sun rose and he saw that the singer was a Lion ("only a lion," as he said to himself) he tried his hardest to make himself believe that it wasn't singing and never had been singing; only roaring as any lion might in a zoo in our own world. Of course it can't really have been singing, he thought, I must have imagined it. I've been letting my nerves get out of order. Who ever heard of a lion singing? And the longer and more beautifully the Lion sang, the harder Uncle Andrew tried to make himself believe that he could hear nothing but roaring. Now the trouble about trying to make yourself stupider than you really are is that you very often succeed. Uncle Andrew did. He soon did hear nothing but roaring in Aslan's song. Soon he couldn't have heard anything else even if he had wanted to. And when at last the Lion spoke and said, "Narnia awake," he didn't hear any words: he heard only a snarl. And when the beasts spoke in answer, he heard only barkings, growlings, bayings, and howlings.[11]

Humility is requisite if we are to think rationally about God and/or science. Let us all keep an open and sharp mind as we seek to know and defend the truth. Let us not give a ground of accusation for those in opposition (Eph 4:27), and let us tear down the intellectual strongholds of the evil one (2 Cor 10:5). And above all, let us call to remembrance Paul's exhortation to the young evangelist:

The Lord's bond-servant must not be quarrelsome, but be kind to all, able to teach, patient when wronged, with gentleness correcting those who are in opposition, if perhaps God may grant them repentance leading to the knowledge of the truth, and they may come to their senses and escape from the snare of the devil, having been held captive by him to do his will (2 Tim 2:24-26).

Having laid the groundwork for our discussion by tearing down faulty notions and distractions, let us now direct our attention to various areas where science and the Bible do agree.

---

[11] C.S. Lewis, *The Chronicles of Narnia, The Magician's Nephew* (New York: Harper Collins, 1983), 136-137.

Thought Questions:

1. Are science and Christianity mutually exclusive?

_____

_____

_____

_____

2. Is the statement, "Science has disproven Christianity!" True or False? Why?

_____

_____

_____

_____

3. What challenges, particularly in the area of academics, may Christians face?

_____

_____

_____

_____

4. What differences exist between operational and origin science?

_____

_____

_____

_____

5. List some benefits of inter-disciplinary learning for Christians, with specific emphasis on the relationship between faith and reason.

_____

_____

_____

_____

CHAPTER 2

God, Science, and Origins

Wimage hat is our origin? And what bearing, if any, does our origin have on our present existence and possible destiny? Can we truly even know our origins? How would we methodically discover these origins?

These are major questions that formulate the foundational basis for our worldview. Much of this involves deep metaphysical reflection and philosophical analysis via the evaluation of massive amounts of evidence that necessarily require interpretation. Oftentimes, the difficulties of this arduous process prove too taxing for most modern minds, given the immense and ever increasing demands on our schedules.

Be sure, however, that we need to take time to lay this critical foundation. Unwillingness on one's personal part to own and develop their worldview will result in one of two consequences: 1) Unceasing vacillation between any and all worldviews[12]; or 2) Adoption of another's worldview, with no personal validation of the reasons for his or her conclusions.[13] These two inevitable consequences are reflected in the world in which we currently live. Truth has become relative because personal worldview foundations are shot, or, at the very least, shabbily laid based on little reflection on origins and destiny. Conversation about crucial matters, far from being effective and invigorating, too often results in frustration, name-calling, muckraking, and all matter of other irrational responses. We find ourselves at a crossroad. We can take the time to allow reason to compel us toward truth vis-à-vis origins, or we can continue in irrationality because we are too busy. So, how do you wish to proceed?

A Rational Consideration of Our Origins

If you desire to proceed with reason, then let's begin with a rational consideration of origins. Imagine if you will, that the present universe were annihilated and replaced with a complete vacuum. Who would reasonably conclude that anything could come into existence to fill the vacuum unless there existed some power in-

---

[12] "As a result, we are no longer to be children, tossed here and there by waves and carried about by every wind of doctrine, by the trickery of men, by craftiness in deceitful scheming" (Eph 4:14).

[13] "I say this so that no one will delude you with persuasive argument . . . See to it that no one takes you captive through philosophy and empty deception, according to the tradition of men, according to the elementary principles of the world, rather than according to Christ" (Col 2:4, 8).

escapably adequate to also produce our own current universe?

In other words, *ex nihilo nihil fit*, or "out of nothing comes nothing," namely, without a sufficient cause outside of that vacuum! We know this to be the case based on ubiquitous experience and observation in the laboratory and outside of it. Our universe and our earth had a beginning, and since they had a beginning, reason dictates that they both had a cause! This, scientists call the Law of Universal Causation. To put it simply, the order we observe in the universe is a matter of basic cause and effect.

Figure 2.1
Francis Bacon

As Francis Bacon, nicknamed the father of modern science, concurred with the ancient philosopher Aristotle, *"It is rightly laid down that 'True knowledge is that which is deduced from causes.'"*[14] Reason, therefore, suggests that a scientific inquiry into origins requires an analysis of causes. This analysis serves as our beginning point for rationally determining our origin, and consequently, our destiny.

Two Primary Options

Figure 2.2

The world is currently ruled by two predominate worldviews that interpret the available evidence for origins in mutually exclusive ways.[15] Rest assured that aligning oneself with one of these two worldviews brings consequences:

If people think something happened in the past—even if it didn't—that assumption influences their choices. This is important to remember: how we view the past directly influences choices we make in the present, which in turn determines the future.[16]

The first school of thought (i.e. Naturalism/Materialism/Evolution[17]) states that matter has always existed, changing forms over time through various undirected and impersonal forces. Astronomer Howard Shapley reflects this view of the beginning by crassly remarking, *"Some piously record 'In the beginning God,' but I say 'In the beginning hydrogen."* His most famous student, Carl Sagan, has influenced an entire generation of thought regarding materialism with his infamous (often educationally mandated reading/watching) work *Cosmos* which opens with: *"THE COSMOS IS ALL THAT IS OR EVER WAS OR EVER WILL BE."* This viewpoint comes with major metaphysical consequences in which all of our human traits are simply the result of *"minor accidents in our immensely long evolutionary history."* Ardent atheist Richard Dawkins candidly reveals the gloomy impact of this viewpoint:

In a universe of blind physical forces and genetic replication, some people are going to get hurt, other people are going to get lucky, and you won't find any rhyme or reason in it, nor any justice. The universe we observe has precisely the properties we should expect if there is, at bottom, no design, no purpose, no evil and no good, nothing but blind, pitiless indifference.[18]

As such, evolution becomes much more than a simple worldview, it becomes a religion. Dr. Michael Ruse, a Canadian philosopher of science makes this clear:

Evolution is promoted by its practitioners as more than mere science. Evolution is promulgated as an ideology, a secular religion—a full-fledged alternative to Christianity, with meaning and morality . . . Evolution is a religion. This

---

[14] Francis Bacon, *Novum Organum* (London: Francis Bacon, 1620), II.2.

[15] Consideration of worldview foundations is crucial for any viewpoint. For a thorough treatment of the Christian worldview, consult: James Porter Moreland and William Lane Craig, *Philosophical Foundations for a Christian Worldview* (Downers Grove, Ill: InterVarsity Press, 2003).

[16] Thomas Purifoy Jr., "The Power of Alternate Histories of the Universe", *Is Genesis History?,,* https://isgenesishistory.com/power-of-alternate-histories-of-universe.

[17] These terms are not necessarily equivalent, but for our purposes we are lumping them together. If so inclined, one may more narrowly define them to draw precise lines of distinction.

[18] Richard Dawkins, *River Out of Eden: A Darwinian View of Life* (London: Phoenix, 1996), 133.

was true of evolution in the beginning, and it is true of evolution still today.[19]

The second school of thought positively believes there is a Governor of the universe, an Unmoved mover (i.e. Supernaturalism). For the purposes of our present work, we will exclusively consider the God of the Bible with regard to this second school of thought. This origin is how the Bible opens: *"In the beginning God created the heavens and the earth"* (Gen 1:1).[20] For clarification, this second school of thought does not dismiss natural order or overlook natural processes in the function of the universe. Rather, this school considers God to order those natural processes and even at times, as deemed appropriate by Him, to manipulate or suspend that natural order to accomplish His purposes (i.e. miracles).

With regards to biblical creationism specifically, it is important to realize that what is commonly sold as truth is not necessarily truth. While biblical creationism is consistently propagandized in the media as being the small fundamental, poorly educated, and stubborn minority, a 1992 Gallop pole revealed that nearly 50% of Americans believed that *"God created man pretty much in his present form at one time within the last 10,000 years."* By contrast, less than 10% of Americans subscribed to the belief that "man has developed over millions of years from less advanced forms of life" by a merely materialistic process. No doubt those statistics would be somewhat different today, but they do describe the nature of the American public within less than a generational span.

While there are other more specific viewpoints on origins (e.g. directed panspermia, oscillating universe, multiverses, etc.), these are clearly not as popular or dominant,[21] nor do they practically address the question of origins. In line with the goal of this book, let us ponder the scientific merits of belief in the God of the Bible and the manifold failures of naturalism to measure up, particularly to the scientific Law of Universal Causation.

---

[19] Michael Ruse, "Saving Darwinism from the Darwinians," *National Post* (May 13, 2000): B-3.

[20] Note that the Bible does <u>NOT</u> begin with an argument for God. The existence of God is viewed as selfevident and axiomatic. This does not require us to dismiss evidential apologetics, for the Bible clearly employs this type of reasoning and defense (e.g. Heb 3:4). For a helpful assessment of apologetic methods, see: Cowan, Steven B., William Lane Craig, John M. Frame, Kelly James Clark, and Paul D. Feinberg. 2000. *Five Views on Apologetics*. Grand Rapids, Mich: Zondervan Pub. House.

[21] The most prominent proselytizers of directed panspermia in particular include Francis Crick (co-discoverer of the double helix structure of DNA) and the infamous astronomer Carl Sagan.

The Argument For God Is the Argument For a First Cause

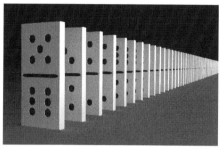

Figure 2.3

In line with the Law of Universal Causation, there must be at least one permanent, uncaused Cause. There cannot rationally be infinite regress. There reasonably follows from this law that there exists some power that is eternal/uncreated, necessary (as an explanation of all others), unconditional (independent), immutable (unchanging), and absolutely self-existing and self-sufficing. Everything that does not exist of absolute and unchangeable necessity must have a sufficient cause. This truth is self-evident and absolutely certain. The Christian believes this is YHWH—the God of the Bible. To frame this in His own words—*"I AM WHO I AM,"* (Exod 3:14), *"I am the Alpha and the Omega,"* (Rev 1:8; 21:6; 22:13), *"And there is no other God besides Me, a righteous God and a Savior; there is none except Me"* (Isa 45:21)."

Oftentimes, this line of evidential reasoning is referred to as the cosmological argument, or expressly as we have framed it, the kalam cosmological argument. William Lane Craig, world-renowned apologist of the Christian faith and recipient of five college degrees including two Master's Degrees and two Doctorates,[22] explains it thus:

> *The kalam cosmological argument is an argument that can be simply formulated. Premise one: Whatever begins to exist has a cause. Things don't come into being from nothing. Two: The universe began to exist. There's good philosophical and scientific evidence that the universe is not eternal in the past, but had a beginning. And from that, it follows, three: Therefore, a cause of the universe exists. And then you do a conceptual analysis of what it is to be a cause of space and time, matter, and energy, and I think you're able to show that a beginningless, uncaused, timeless, spaceless, immaterial, enormously powerful, personal creator of the universe exists, which is the core concept of God.[23]*

---

[22] I mention these educational credentials to highlight the fact that thinking people with brilliant minds can and do believe in God, despite common criticisms. The educational credentials of all quoted in this work could likewise be enumerated (some will, but not all). I trust that if any doubts regarding their rational faculties and abilities are alleged, that they will quickly be remedied by research into each individual.

[23] William Lane Craig, "What is the Kalam Cosmological Argument", *The One Minute Apologist*, n.p.[cited 30 September 2018]. Online: https://www.reasonablefaith.org/videos/interviews-panels/what-is-the-kalamcosmological- argument-bobby-conway.

In contrast to this argument, materialists, namely atheists, believe the universe (or its seed) is eternal.[24] This allegedly answers and/or removes the difficulty of origins, but leaves more questions than answers and is based on an unfounded and unobserved presupposition, namely methodological naturalism.[25] If the universe is materially eternal, material self-explanation is requisite. This is why proponents of this paradigm are so eager to prove macroevolution. Proving this theory would rule God out of the picture; however, macroevolution is yet to be proven and, as such, remains a tentative theory, rather than a law. Macroevolution, in truth, is a theory rooted in a naturalistic worldview that a priori dismisses the possibility of God;[26] macroevolution is not a fact established by science.

Molecular biologist and physician Michael Denton summarizes this truth, *"Naturalism is still, as it was in Darwin's time, a highly speculative hypothesis entirely without direct factual support and very far from that self-evident axiom some of its more aggressive advocates would have us believe."* [27]

Professional investigative journalist and former naturalist Lee Strobel keenly observes:

What looks at first blush like an airtight scientific case for evolution begins to unravel upon closer examination. New discoveries during the past thirty years have prompted an increasing number of scientists to contradict Darwin by concluding that there was an Intelligent Designer behind the creation and development of life.[28]

He also states: *"My road to atheism was paved by science . . . But, ironically, so was my later journey to God."*[29]

---

[24] Note that either viewpoint has to identify a foundation. The elephant must be named. Consult: Sire, James W. Sire, *Naming the Elephant: Worldview As a Concept* (Downers Grove, IL: IVP Academic, 2015).

[25] Alvin Plantinga defines and critiques this philosophical commitment: *"The philosophical doctrine of methodological naturalism holds that, for any study of the world to qualify as 'scientific,' it cannot refer to God's creative activity (or any sort of divine activity). The methods of science, it is claimed, 'give us no purchase' on theological propositions--even if the latter are true—and theology therefore cannot influence scientific explanation or theory justification. Thus, science is said to be religiously neutral, if only because science and religion are, by their very natures, epistemically distinct. However, the actual practice and content of science challenge this claim. In many areas, science is anything but religiously neutral; moreover, the standard arguments for methodological naturalism suffer from various grave shortcomings."* (Origins & Design 18:1; http://www.arn.org/docs/odesign/od181/methnat181.htm).

[26] One scientist provides a clear example of this prejudicial line of scientific reasoning when he states: *"Science must be provisionally atheistic or cease to be itself."* (Robert T. Pennock, Intelligent Design: Creationism and its Critics (Cambridge, MA: The MIT Press, 2001), 144.)

Michael Behe, renowned biochemist out of Lehigh University in Bethlehem, Pennsylvania, has also added to the flames:

The conclusion of intelligent design flows naturally from the data itself—not from sacred books or sectarian beliefs . . . The reluctance of science to embrace the conclusion of intelligent design . . . has no justifiable foundation . . . Many people, including many important and well-respected scientists, just don't want there to be anything beyond nature.[30]

Well-known bio-informaticist Hupert P. Jockey candidly remarks,

Since science does not have the faintest idea how life on earth originated . . . it would only be honest to confess this to other scientists, to grantors, and to the public at large. Prominent scientists speaking ex cathedra, should refrain from polarizing the minds of students and young productive scientists with statements that are based solely on beliefs.[31]

What Do Science And Reason Show?

Antony Flew, former atheist of yesteryear, admitted in his seminal work, *"the universe is something that begs an explanation."*[32] That the universe exists declares a cause for its existence! Science is unanimously agreed that the earth had a beginning; what they debate is the how. Even the favored Big Bang Theory has fallen into disrepute in recent years because it is totally unsupported by science and is merely the result of a philosophy that dismisses the possibility of God a priori.[33] Let's consider what science actually shows.

First, if the earth had no beginning, all radioactive materials and isotopes would

---

[27] Michael Denton, *Evolution: A Theory in Crisis* (Bethesda: Adler & Adler, 1986), 77.

[28] Lee Strobel, *The Case for Faith: A Journalist Investigates the Toughest Objections to Christianity* (Grand Rapids, Mich: Zondervan, 2004), 90.

[9] Lee Strobel and Garry Poole, *The Case for a Creator: A Six-Session Investigation of the Scientific Evidence That Points Toward God* (Grand Rapids, Mich.: Zondervan, 2008).

[30] Michael J. Behe, *Darwin's Black Box* (New York: The Free Press, 2006), 193, 251, 243.

[31] Hupert P. Jockey, *Journal of Theoretical Biology* 91 (1981): 13.

[32] Antony Flew, *There Is a God: How The World's Most Notorious Atheist Changed His Mind* (New York: Harper Collins, 2007), 145.

[33] The *New Scientist* magazine published an open letter entitled "Bucking the big bang" on May 22, 2004 rejecting the Big Bang Theory. The letter was signed by hundreds of scientists, most of which were atheists!

be gone! Because elements break down based on half-life, atoms of this proton, neutron, and electron magnitude, combined with their instability, would have necessarily broken down into smaller elements. Since these elements are still around, the earth cannot be billions of years old as the naturalist arrogantly postures!

Second, scientists across the board agree that there are telltale signs that incredible generation took place at the creation of our universe. Without becoming overly scientific, it has to do with radiation heat signatures (called an afterglow) and ripples from those signatures. Far from proving the Big Bang, these ripples are *"machining marks*

Figure 2.4

from the creation of the universe" and *"the fingerprints of the maker,"* according to astronomer George Smoot, who was the project leader for the COBE satellite.[34]

Third, naturalists believe in spontaneous generation of life from non-life (called biopoiesis or abiogenesis), but this is a direct violation of the scientific Law of Biogenesis.[35] Abiogenesis (aka biopoiesis) has not once been observed, even in the laboratory. Mankind, for many years, falsely believed in spontaneous generation of bacteria and maggots in rotten meat, but, as science developed, so did our understanding of why and how these life forms truly generated in total corroboration of biogenesis![36]

Figure 2.5 Louis Pasteur

Fourth, if you find a watch lying in the grass and it is still running, you know it has not lain there for all eternity. Given the naturalist's ever fluctuating and extending timeline of the universe, the laws of thermodynamics (especially entropy) would have resulted in the dissolution of the universe. Christian apologist Doy Moyer explains this basic failure of naturalism:

---

[34] Fred Heeren, Show Me God: What the Message from Space Is Telling Us About God (Wheeling, IL: Day Star Publications, 2000), 168.

[35] Louis Pasteur famously formulated this law when he said, "Life can only come from life."

[36] Stanley Miller's "synthesis" of amino acids has proven nothing. He freely admitted that he manipulated the environment in which he created these amino acids. Consequently, rather than showing abiogenesis, he in effect demonstrated intelligent design.

According to the second law of thermodynamics, processes that occur within a closed system tend toward a state of equilibrium (or decay). With no energy being fed into the system, everything would eventually "burn up" and wear out. So how does this help the believer's cause? Well the question is simple: if, given enough time, the universe would burn out (reach "heat death"), then why hasn't it already happened if it did not have a beginning? Assuming that the universe is infinite, it should have already burned out. Yet, here we are. Here, unbelievers must propose a model that is neither scientifically provable nor observed anywhere. The universe cannot be eternal.[37]

Science and reason, as a matter of fact, do not support naturalism in this way or in any other way, as we will see in our continued proceedings. Although the publicity goes to atheistic scientists, much like the publicity goes to progressive liberals, there is a hugely significant movement in science towards creationism. In actuality, there are hundreds of statements of faith signed by thousands of scientists!

Theologian W.A. Criswell brings up a historical point worthy of consideration in this regard:

In 1861 . . . the French Academy of Science published a little brochure in which they stated fifty-one facts that controverted the Word of God. Today, there is not a scientist in the world who believes a single one of those fifty-one so-called scientific facts that in 1861 were published as controverting the Word of God. Not a one!"[38]

Notice, this statement was made a little over 150 years ago! The truth is that

Figure 2.6

For the scientist who has lived by faith in the power of reason, the story ends like a bad dream. He has scaled the mountains of ignorance; he is about to conquer the highest peak; as he pulls himself over the final rock, he is greeted by a band of theologians who have been sitting there for centuries.[39]

---

[37] Doy Moyer, *Mind Your Faith: Essays in Apologetics* (Temple Terrace, FL: Florida College Press, 2010), 145.

[38] W.A. Criswell, *The Bible for Today's World* (Grand Rapids: Zondervan, 1966), 30.

[39] Robert Jastrow, *God and the Astronomers* (New York: Norton, 1978), 116.

The Link Between Cosmology And Epistemology

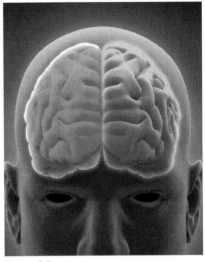

Figure 2.7

An outgrowth of the origins discussion is the fact that man is acutely and singularly aware of his existence. As with our earlier cosmological discussion, there are two possible explanations—eternal Mind or eternal matter. This fundamentally represents the epistemological grounds upon which we build our worldview. Where did this knowledge and awareness originate? He who denies the existence of God is affirming that matter created our present world. Atheists scoff at the idea of God, but must believe in the eternal existence of matter. The atheist must believe that the order found in nature is the result of chance or fate; that consciousness arose from unconscious matter. Scientists at the top of their respective fields willingly concede that this is impossible.

Something happened in the past that is not happening now—the Earth began. When we consider the classic go-to theory for the scientific community, the Big Bang, and we measure it against what we scientifically and by common sense know, it falls disastrously short.[40] Who would reasonably argue that the largest explosion in the history of the universe resulted in such complex arrangement and order? Everything we know about ballistics and explosives militates against this theory! Every explosion we know, on a small scale or large scale, results in disorder; in fact, the larger the explosion, the greater the disorder. So explain again how the largest explosion in the history of the universe could result in what at the very least appears to be emphatically orderly? Even scientists are jettisoning this view and admitting it's nothing more than crackpot philosophy bigoted against the possibility

---

[40] Sir Fred Hoyle comments very negatively on the place of big bang cosmologies: *"But the interesting quark transformations are almost immediately over and done with, to be followed by a little rather simple nuclear physics, to be followed by what? By a dull-as-ditchwater expansion which degrades itself adiabatically until it is incapable of doing anything at all. The notion that galaxies form, to be followed by an active astronomical history, is an illusion. Nothing forms, the thing is as dead as a door-nail...The punch line is that, even though outward speeds are maintained in a free explosion, internal motions die away adiabatically, and the expanding system becomes inert, which is exactly why the big-bang cosmologies lead to a universe that is dead-and-donewith almost from the beginning."* (Hoyle, Fred. "The Big Bang in Astronomy," New Scientist (Nov. 19, 1981): 523-524.)

of a Governor of lives and over the universe. There is no rational reason why any nation should deny God, for *"He has not left Himself without witness"* (Acts 14:17). So knowledge really is not the key issue; rejection of God is rendered a matter of volition because, epistemologically, the Christian has the upper hand.

The classic swipe taken by atheists is the question: *"Well, where did God come from? Who created him?"* This question is framed incorrectly, which is why it is nonsensical. We argue that every *dependent* thing must have a cause—the kalam cosmological argument. God is not dependent according to Christianity; He is necessary. And by faith, Christians know Him as Creator (Heb 11:3).

The Nature of the First Cause

The First Cause is transcendent. The Cause is greater than the result (cf. Heb 3:3-4; Acts 17:24). As we have seen already, being the First Cause makes the Source eternal. This is one of the foundational realities of the biblical God.

The First Cause is personal and intelligent. God must possess intelligence and volition. Since God has a mind and has shared His mind (cf. 1 Cor 2:10-13), He cannot be viewed as impersonal.

The First Cause has power beyond the comprehension of human minds. Creating from nothing is beyond us. We can only manipulate things. Think: Gen 1.

The First Cause has some relationship to and understanding of morality. That humans have a basic sense of right and wrong suggests that our source has that

Figure 2.8

sense as well although, outside of the Bible, we have no real understanding of whether the Source is good or evil. Strict naturalism has no explanation for this. In fact, strict atheism ultimately breaks down morally and judicially. Either there is a non-material realm or there is no moral realm of responsibility! We will return to this idea in Chapter 12.

There can only be one first cause. The universe is so well tuned that a single cause is necessary (cf. 1 Cor 14:33). We will also consider this in further detail at a later point.

Concluding Thoughts And Summation

In an essay published in 1954, Albert Einstein famously remarked: *"Science without religion is lame; religion without science is blind."* There is perhaps no greater illustration of the truth of this statement than in the scientific discussion of origins.

There is simply no cosmological excuse for being an atheist. As the psalmists commonly remarked: *"The fool has said in his heart, 'There is no god.'"* (e.g. Pss 14:1; 53:1). Knowledge of God's creative power is self-evident in nature (Rom 1:20). God is the Author of those faculties of reason that lead all honest persons to believe in Him and in His creation of the universe. However, we cannot learn conclusively about God and His personal love without the final revelation of His Son (Heb 1:1-2). And God's will for you is in His Son. This of course falls into the category of history, which complements the inescapable conclusion of legitimate scientific inquiry—*"God exists and He is the rewarder of those who diligently seek Him"* (Heb 11:6).

Thought Questions:

1. Define cosmology.

_____

_____

_____

_____

2. Give three reasons why knowing our origin is important.

_____

_____

_____

_____

3. Compare and contrast the two prominent viewpoints on origins.

_____

_____

_____

_____

4. What information does the Bible give regarding the origin of humans?

_____

_____

_____

_____

5. Is a consideration of origins a biblical study, a scientific study, neither, or both?

_____

_____

_____

_____

CHAPTER 3

The Age
of the Earth

Christians take many viewpoints that are hostile to the world's status quo. One of the most hated and antagonistic viewpoints that Christians are to defend is the biblical age of the Earth. This stems from the irreconcilable differences that exist between the biblical and naturalistic cosmologies as discussed in the previous chapter. Many, led by evolutionary theorists, will prove to be belligerent toward the biblical view of the age of the Earth, ridiculing Christians as irrational. Rather than be dismissive or, God-forbid, respond in kind, Christians are called to defend this biblical truth, as it is an important aspect of the whole counsel of God. This, Christians can do and should be willing to do. As the wise man Solomon writes by inspiration: *"The heart of the righteous ponders how to answer, but the mouth of the wicked pours out evil things"* (Prov 15:28). There are major consequences in this defense and in what can result in our own deception by the influence of these critics and scoffers. This chapter will address the age of the Earth, contrast the evolutionary viewpoint with the biblical viewpoint, and warn of the perils of compromise.

The Materialistic/Naturalistic/Evolutionary Viewpoint

Currently, most proponents of this view fervidly date the universe to around thirteen-fourteen billion years old. Earth itself is dated to around 4.5 billion years old. Important to note is the historical fact that this dating fluctuates every few years or so, namely, the age keeps getting older! To illustrate, in the days of Charles Darwin, evolutionists believed the Earth was twenty million years old. Naturalists willingly admit the date gets longer and longer because more forms are discovered in the fossil record, thus requiring more transitional intermediaries, thus requiring more time. The tenuousness of naturalistic dating begs the question. How reliable are the current dates if they are subject to change, possibly exponentially, within a few decades? Further, if these dates are so tenuous, what does this say of the pretentiousness and snobbery of naturalistic intellectuals as they pompously posit these dates?[41] So, how is this dating "scientifically" derived?

---

[41] Francis Crick illustrates: *"A knowledge of the true age of the Earth and the fossil record makes it impossible for any balanced intellect to believe in the literal truth of every part of the Bible the way that fundamentalists do"* (Francis Crick, *What Mad Pursuit: A Personal View of Scientific Discovery* (New York: Basic Books, 1988), 11.) To which we reply with the words of Socrates: *"When the debate is lost, slander becomes the tool of the losers."*

Figure 3.1 Geological Time Spiral

Naturalistic Dating Methods And Issues

The typical methods of ascertaining age include: Radiometric/Radioisotope Dating (Carbon, Argon, etc.), Ice Core Dating, and Isochron Dating. Each of these methods is fraught with major issues of inconsistency that go unmentioned as the dates are codified as "scientifically proven."

Figure 3.2 Francis Crick

Regarding the measurement of half-life and isotopic measurements, there are numerous reasons to be skeptical of these methods.[42] In sum, they are totally unreliable and inconsistent. Why? Let's summarize. The poster-child for these methods is carbon dating. Yet, carbon dating doesn't even agree with the evolutionary dating system! Why? Because Carbon-14 is undetectable after 100,000 years! Additionally, retesting and blind testing of samples results in vastly different assessments.

Cross-method and cross-isotope testing renders up to a billion years difference in the same sample! Furthermore, unprovable assumptions abound including, but not limited to, initial conditions being known (e.g. the zero date problem), constant decay rates, and no leaching or addition of parent/daughter isotopes. None of these assumptions is factually known but is presupposed; science has recurrently called into question every single one of these assumptions!

Now let's consider Ice Core Dating. Geologists assume layers are laid down based on snowfall and climate, fair enough. However, as with the other methods, this rests on the presupposition of Uniformitarianism. In point of fact, examples are abundant to illustrate that these and other assumptions with this method are unfounded. One prominent example is the recent discovery of two P-38 Lightning warplanes from WWII underneath hundreds of feet of ice in Greenland.[43] The fundamental assumptions of Ice Core Dating render this placement impossible.[44]

Various other issues abound including sedimentation rates, Earth's decreasing magnetic field, atmospheric Helium rates, continued existence of short-period comets, population growth, etc., but let's dig more into the underlying and problematic interpretive biases of evolutionary dating methods to break down main substructure.

Naturalistic Interpretive Biases

The foremost assumption of naturalistic dating is Uniformitarianism. This is the belief that the way all things operate now is the way they have always operated. Did you know that the Bible not only reveals this to be historically untrue, but also specifically condemns this assumption? Peter, the Apostle of the Lord, write by inspiration of the Spirit and says,

> *Know this first of all, that in the last days mockers will come with their mocking, following after their own lusts, and saying, 'Where is the promise of His coming? For ever since the fathers fell asleep, all continues just as it was from the beginning of creation.' For when they maintain this, it escapes their notice that by the word of God the heavens existed long ago and the earth was formed*

---

[42] This section is primarily indebted to information provided in the interviews conducted in the *New Answers DVD's* produced by *Answers in Genesis*. Unless otherwise specified, quotes in this section are sourced from these interviews.

[43] The first was recovered in August 1992 at a depth of 260 feet and was nicknamed "Glacier Girl." The second was discovered at a depth of over 300 feet in 2011 and has since been confirmed by radar. Scientists hope to recover the plane imminently.

[44] Jake Herbert, "WWII Plane Found Frozen In Greenland Ice," Institute for Creation Research, http://www.icr.org/article/wwii-plane-found-frozen-in-greenland-ice.

out of water and by water, through which the world at that time was destroyed, being flooded with water. But by His word the present heavens and earth are being reserved for fire, kept for the day of judgment and destruction of ungodly men (2 Pet 3:3-7).

Allegiance to Uniformitarianism ignores the effects of Catastrophism. The Word of God relates that major changes have occurred since the beginning of time. Among these are most notably the Fall of Adam and Eve in the Garden of Eden and the entrance of sin into the world (Gen 3; Rom 8:20-22) as well as Noah's Flood (Gen 6-9). Rather than using the present as a key to the past (i.e. Uniformitarianism), we should be using the past as a key to understanding the present! Let's not put the cart before the horse!

Figure 3.3 Grand Canyon

Let's illustrate several observed examples of the effects of Catastrophism. First, we have the Grand Canyon. Catastrophism is the only tenable explanation for the Grand Canyon as the Colorado River does not erode its channel. Why? The topography and timeline for the formulation of the canyon system are prohibitive.[45] Consequently, the breathtaking landform had to be caused by rapid catastrophic erosion. Second, consider the massive Mount St. Helens eruption in 1980. This eruption laid down six hundred feet of rock layers as a result! Two years later, on March 18, 1982, a

Figure 3.4 Mount St. Helens, top before, above, after

---

[45] Scientists universally agree on three key observations that justify this argument: 1) the plateau was there before the Colorado River which creates a problem because the headwaters of the river are at a lower elevation than the plateau itself thus requiring water to go uphill to carve the canyon; 2) the scope of the erosion is 1,000 square miles; and 3) the canyon displays rapid and catastrophic erosion.

canyon system 1/40 scale of Grand Canyon with walls one hundred feet high was created by a mudflow in the area in twenty-four hours!

A third assumption is the unwarranted dismissal of eyewitness testimony and explanation. Two quotes serve to illustrate.

The Bible claims to be the communication to us of the Creator God who has always existed. Its authenticity is overwhelmingly verified . . . In Genesis 1-11, it is revealed how to calculate the age of the earth, and how rock layers and fossils were rapidly and recently formed in the year-long, global, catastrophic Flood. (Andrew Snelling, PhD Geology, Director of Research at *Answers in Genesis*)

Figure 3.5

The Bible reveals that Creation speaks to us about the existence of God and some of the attributes of God, but it doesn't tell us that we can work out a history of the world just by looking at the Creation. We cannot trust what sinful scientists, who are using anti-biblical assumptions to interpret the cursed Creation. We cannot use their interpretation to interpret the Bible. Rather we must use the Bible to interpret the world we live in. (Terry Mortenson, MDiv, PhD History of Geology)

Figure 3.6

Truly, *"There is no wisdom and no understanding and no counsel against the Lord"* (Prov 21:30).

The Biblical Viewpoint

Conservative biblical creationists, who read the Bible as it stands, date the Universe and Earth between six thousand and seven thousand years old. No more, no less. This is sometimes referred to as "Young Earth Creationism." This is in marked contrast to "Old Earth Creationism" which is usually synonymous with theistic evolution, which we will address momentarily. But first, how is this dating derived?

Biblical Evidence

According to the Genesis narrative, the heavens and the earth are only five days older than man (Gen 1:24-31). Therefore, if we date mankind, we date the earth and the heavens. So how do we date mankind? Where do we start?

While not the most glamorous portions of Scriptures, genealogies help narrowly define the age of mankind. Genesis is literarily structured around genealogies and nations in what is referred to as a *toledot* formula.[46] For example, we see the Hebrew word at such important transitions in Genesis as in chapters 4 and 5 where Cain and Adam's genealogies are related. We also see the Hebrew word at the transition in the Table of Nations in chapter 10 as mankind populates the Earth and we are led into the genealogy of Abraham in Genesis 11. No doubt, though, the most extensive genealogy is contained in the first eight chapters of 1 Chronicles Certainly the simpler genealogies to comprehend are those connected to Christ in Matt 1 and Luke 3. When compared with these other genealogies, Luke's pedigree of Jesus provides a helpful timeline of human history by relating the twenty generations comprising two millennia between Adam and Abraham (3:34-38) and the fifty five generations over two millennia between Abraham and Christ (3:23-34). Since two millennia have passed since the time of Christ, we have a grand sum of six thousand years, give or take a few possible decades. Add five days and that is the age of the heavens and the earth!

But what are "days"? Liberal Bible theologians with macroevolutionary sentiments often call into question the meaning of "day" in Genesis. Simple examination reveals this to be motivated by philosophy and worldview rather than fact. The Creation account clearly defines "day" by "morning" and "evening" in Gen 1. "Day" is used figuratively in verses that speak to the timelessness of God (e.g. 2 Pet 3:8), but Gen 1 is clearly not in this context. Even if it were, we would have thousands of years, not billions. Steven H. Boyd, PhD Hebrew Language, summarizes,

> *The world's greatest Hebraists are unanimously agreed that Genesis 1-2 is a narrative. This is utterly unique because all creation accounts in ANE are written in epic poetry. If we start with the text, yom means day. We have to project something foreign into the text to get anything otherwise.*[47]

There is zero evidence to support the belief that a figurative usage is in mind in Gen 1. Add to that the undeniable treatment of the seventh day as literal in the Decalogue –

> *Remember the sabbath day, to keep it holy. Six days you shall labor and do all your work, but the seventh day is a sabbath of the Lord your God; in it you shall not do any work, you or your son or your daughter, your male or your female servant or your cattle or your sojourner who stays with you. For in six days the Lord made the heavens and the earth, the sea and all that is in them,*

---

[46] For discussion on the significance of this formula to the framework of Genesis, consult: Nahum M. Sarna, 1989. *Genesis: The Traditional Hebrew Text with the New JPS Translation = Be-Rêšît* (Philadelphia: Jewish Publication Society, 1989), 16.

[47] *Is Genesis History?*, DVD, directed by Thomas Purifoy, Jr. (Newtown, PA: Virgil Films, 2017).

and rested on the seventh day; therefore the Lord blessed the sabbath day and made it holy (Exod 20:8-11).

The Genesis account is also unanimously considered by biblical figures as the real, actual, and factual beginning. The supreme example of this is Jesus, who clearly views Genesis 1 in that way (Matt 19:6; 23:35; 24:37-38). He would know since He was an eyewitness! (Gen 1:26; John 1:1; Col 1:16)! Paul serves as another clear example of this viewpoint as he uses Adam and Eve as a basis for his inspired teachings (e.g. 1 Cor 11:3, 8; 2 Cor 11:3; 1 Tim 2:12-14).

Scientific Evidence[48]

Population studies and population genetics have unequivocally shown the common descent of all mankind.[49] They have also shown that if mankind were even one million years old, the population would be 10^{5000}. This is more people than could actually fit on the surface of the earth! Using the same population formula, the Bible timeline suggests a world population of five-ten billion, which accurately matches the current figures.

Geologists have also come to some Bible-affirming conclusions based on studies of erosion and weathering. For example, at the current observable erosion rates, all of the continents would have completely eroded in fourteen million years, thus undermining naturalistic views on Earth's timeline. One example demonstrating the reasonability of biblical creationism is the Mississippi River, which deposits three hundred million cubic yards of sediment into the Gulf of Mexico every year. The observable accumulation at the delta reveals a date of about four thousand years.

Measurements, calculations, and scientific findings also abound in the realm of astronomy. One curious consideration weighing in the favor of biblical creationism is the observed shrinkage of the Sun. Astrophysicists determined in 1979 that the Sun was shrinking at a rate of 0.1% every one hundred years. Based on this data, the Sun would have been twice its current size one hundred thousand years ago and at that same rate, the Earth would have been inside the Sun twenty million years ago. In light of this, could Earth be 4.5 billion years old as naturalists claim? Impossible! Cosmic dust accumulation is another interesting field of study. Earth is hit by fourteen million tons of space materials every year. If the Earth were 4.5 bil-

---

[48] This section is indebted to: Heath Rogers, *Introduction to Christian Evidences* (Bowling Green, KY: One Stone, 2017).

[49] Compare Acts 17:26 which reads: *"and He made from one man every nation of mankind to live on all the face of the earth, having determined their appointed times and the boundaries of their habitation."*

lion years old, there would be 182 feet of meteor dust all over the Earth. There was not even $^1/_8$ inch of dust on the moon during the Apollo missions! Thirdly, according to Astronomer Danny Faulkner and other creation astronomers, spiral galactic structures, of which the Milky Way Galaxy and Andromeda Galaxy are classified, suggest a young Earth. If the universe was as old as naturalists commonly assert, the spiral structures would have dissipated much like cocoa powder mixed into a brownie recipe.[50]

Difficulties?

Are there difficulties Christians have to deal with when taking the literal biblical view? Yes. For instance, the Earth appears old. In reality, this is not a problem. According to the Genesis narrative, Adam was created, not as a baby, but as a mature adult, capable of procreation. Animals, plants, and the Earth were created similarly. Moreover, and as discussed in the previous chapter, Catastrophism is a viable explanation for the apparent age of the earth, coal deposits, mass fossil deposits, and geological formations (as will be discussed in Chapters 5-6). Another commonly cited issue is that the biblical dating does not align with commonly used scientific dating techniques. But again, this is not a true problem given the inaccuracy of such techniques and the skewed interpretations of presupposition-laden evolutionary scientists.

What about the stars? Biblical creationism believes in a timeline of six thousand years, yet we see starlight from distances requiring more time. The Sun is ninety-three million miles away. Light travels at 186,000 miles per second meaning light from the sun takes eight minutes and twenty seconds to travel to Earth. The next closest star is actually a triple-star system known as Alpha Centauri, which is held together by gravity. This system is over four light years away. But as we continue to get farther from Earth, we start pressing the timeline. The farthest star we can see with the naked eye is V762 Cas in Cassiopeia at 16,308 light years away. This is more than double the biblical timeline of the earth and that is just for the stars we can see with the naked eye! With the assistance of advanced telescopes, we can see exponentially further. So, how do biblical creationists explain this discrepancy (i.e. the "light travel time problem")? Or can they?

Several possibilities resolve this issue. Let's consider just a few. God could have created the universe and then stretched it. This would mean starlight did not re-

[50] *Is Genesis History?*, DVD, directed by Thomas Purifoy, Jr. (Newtown, PA: Virgil Films, 2017).

[51] *"Let there be lights in the expanse of the heavens to separate the day from the night, and let them be for signs and for seasons and for days and years; and let them be for lights in the expanse of the heavens to give light on the earth"; and it was so. God made the two great lights, the greater light to govern the day, and the lesser light to govern the night; He made the stars also"* (Gen 1:14-16).

quire as much time to travel. Another possibility posited by creationist scientists is that the speed of light has not always been constant (a hypothesis known as CDK). A very simple way to consider this from a biblical perspective would be that God created the universe, including the stars on the fourth day, and then chose to speed the light up to reach the Earth to the end that they would serve their specified purpose.[51] Yet another theory for reconciliation considers the fluidity of calculating time (Alternate Synchrony Conventions, ASC). Even on Earth, we render time with some relative difference. Calendars have not always been universal, although they are more so in recent years. Time zones render different times of day based on location. We also have daylight savings time. Perhaps anti-entropic time zones exist in space. Other creation scientists have posited Gravitational Time Dilation (GTD; i.e. the universe ages at a different rate than the Earth because gravity slows down time per General Relativity), Carmelian physics, and various other possibilities. One, none, or all of these possibilities may hold some key to unlock this alleged discrepancy. The problem for biblical creationism is clearly not without resolution.[52]

Theistic Evolution and Why It's a Dangerous Sham[53]

The inspired Apostle Paul warns Christians of antiquity:

But I am afraid that, as the serpent deceived Eve by his craftiness, your minds will be led astray from the simplicity and purity of devotion to Christ. For if one comes and preaches another Jesus whom we have not preached, or you receive a different spirit which you have not received, or a different gospel which you have not accepted, you bear this beautifully (2 Cor 11:3-4).

He is concerned that the Corinthians had been led astray by deception. This concern and warning are especially fitting for advocates of theistic evolution who have conformed themselves to the world rather than allow God to transform their minds through renewal (Rom 12:1-2).

The basic idea of theistic evolution is that God used macroevolution as the means of creating life on Earth. What motivates this amalgamation? Well, evolution is viewed as indisputable fact. Why? Because of aggressive marketing, in-

---

[52] The published works and lectures of astronomer Jason Lisle are especially helpful in this discussion.

[53] Many of the critiques in this section would also, in principle, apply to those who espouse Christianity while also espousing the Big Bang Theory. Trying to merge atheistic interpretations into the Bible is akin to Israel wanting to incorporate pagan ideas (e.g. 1 Sam 8).

doctrination, and intellectual intimidation.[54] If you do not subscribe to macro-evolutionary theory, you are labeled a dunce who cannot possibly be accepted as a reasonable person (see the first footnote of this chapter). Intellectual elitism and an air of intellectual bravado is also cloaked in technical nomenclature and shrouded in Latin. This is done in part to intimidate those who are unacquainted with such terminology. Clearly, this method is highly effective in the perpetuation of misinformation and causes resolution to ignorance. People often just "take it for granted" or believe it is "beyond dispute."

So, how do espousing Bible believers accommodate the vast amounts of time required by macroevolution into the Genesis account? Two ways primarily. First, advocates of "Gap Theory" claim there is an unmentioned and massive gap between Gen 1:1 and 1:2. Second, advocates of "Day-Age Theory" claim each day of Creation was not actually a day as we see days today, a claim that is biblically refuted above.

Macroevolution and Gen 1 are simply irreconcilable. Compromising plain biblical truth to accommodate a manmade theory is not only unnecessary, but extremely dangerous. As Andrew Snelling keenly observes, *"The outcome of letting Scripture interpret Scripture is a young earth and universe."* When we do that, we will confidently say, *"I have more insight than all my teachers for Your testimonies are my meditation"* (Ps 119:99).

Concluding Thought:
Does the Subject of the Age of the Earth Matter?

The Earth's age is important. It tells us how we are to view knowledge, science, and the Bible. It determines how we read the Bible and how we interpret the Bible (correctly or incorrectly). As Ken Ham has so candidly remarked, *"to believe in millions of years is a gospel issue. This belief ultimately impugns the character of the Creator and Savior and undermines the foundation of the soul-saving gospel.*[55]

The Bible clearly teaches that mankind was created in the beginning, around 6,000 years ago. Evolution clearly teaches something very different. If we are going to have the correct view of God, we need to take the Bible as the supreme authority. Make no mistake, millions of years is an attack on Jesus Christ.

Compromising God's truth always proves perilous (Deut 4:2; Prov 30:6; Rev

---

[54] Reading to my toddler, I recently came across naturalistic timeframes in the *Magic School Bus* series as well as *Arthur the Aardvark*. What a sad and repugnant testimony to the evolutionary brainwashing of children!

[55] Ken Ham, "Millions of Years—Are Souls at Stake?" *Answers In Genesis,* https://answersingenesis.org/theory-of-evolution/millions-of-years/are-souls-at-stake.

22:18f); *"Once we start down the road of compromise, it'll take us further than we ever intended to go."*[56] Again,

> As soon as you surrender the Bible's authority in one area, you 'unlock the door' to do the same thing in other areas. Once the door of compromise is open, even if ajar just a little, subsequent generations push the door open wider. Ultimately, this compromise has been a major contributing factor in the loss of biblical authority in our Western world.[57]

As always, with any study of Creation, let us, having engaged in this study, develop a mature sense of awe and appreciation for God's supreme power and sovereignty, for His steady hand, and for His kindness in the exaltation of mankind. God created the universe in six days out of nothing!

You may be thinking one of several things to yourself. You may be captured in awe at God's grandeur. You may be convicted by having taken the wrong view on Creation, the age of the Earth, or God's role in that Creation. Perhaps you have compromised the truth out of ignorance, unwillingness to study, or were afraid to challenge what you have been told. God expects us to love Him with all of our minds[58] and to trust Him with all of our heart.[59] Take God at His word and learn to defend the faith!

---

[56] Rogers, *Introduction to Christian Evidences*, 34.

[57] Ken Ham, 2013. *The New Answers Book Volume 4: Over 30 Questions on Creation/Evolution and the Bible* (Green Forest, AR: New Leaf Publishing Group, 2013), 18.

[58] *"You shall love the Lord your God with all your heart, and with all your soul, and with all your strength, and with all your mind . . . Do this and you shall live"* (Luke 10:27-28).

[59] *"Trust in the Lord with all your heart and do not lean on your own understanding. In all your ways acknowledge Him, and He will make your paths straight"* (Prov 3:5-6).

Thought Questions:

1. Does the age of the Earth matter? Support your answer.

_____

_____

_____

_____

2. What evidence supports the naturalistic dating of the Earth? What evidence supports the biblical dating of the Earth?

_____

_____

_____

_____

3. What biases and assumptions undergird naturalistic dating methods?

_____

_____

_____

_____

4. What pitfalls should all be aware of in this discussion?

_____

_____

_____

_____

5. What does the most important commandment require of our minds? How does Proverbs 3:5-6 relate to this?

_____

_____

_____

_____

CHAPTER 4

Dinosaurs: Friends or Foe for Christians?

When discussing origins and the age of the Earth, we inevitably find ourselves transition into the fascinating topic of dinosaurs. Dinosaurs have long captivated the minds of mankind. Movies, cartoons, and other cinema have profited billions of dollars exhibiting these incredible creatures on-screen. And how many of us can remember playing with dinosaur figures when we were younger? Dinosaurs are neat creatures!

Now, technically speaking, dinosaurs refer specifically to land-dwelling creatures of ages past. Sea creatures and flying creatures are categorized differently, although most non-professionals overlook that distinction. Our discussion will use the broad, non-professional sense, unless absolutely necessary to use the technical sense.

We must discuss dinosaurs because it is commonly avowed in textbooks, colleges, high schools, museums, and other centers and avenues of learning that dinosaurs prove Christianity wrong, or at the very least, their existence in epochs past requires monkeying with the biblical text. In fact, I myself was accosted as ignorant of this "scientific fact" several years ago while handing out Bibles in front of the University of South Florida Library. It is quite helpful for Christians who desire to make a defense of Christianity or non-Christians with a desire to con-

Figure 4.1 Detail of the Nile Mosaic of Palestrina, Italy dates to the 1st century BC.

sider the evidence for Christianity, to consider dinosaurs, particularly how they relate to the timeline of the Earth and human history. Our discussion in this chapter will center on three key areas: vindication of the Bible's claim of the coexistence of humans and dinosaurs, dinosaurs in the Bible, and what happened to the dinosaurs. So, let's dig in!

Did Dinosaurs Co-Exist with Man?

Evolutionary scientists have repeatedly berated biblical creationists as ignorant, bamboozled morons in the discussion on dinosaurs. This vilification, combined with secular pragmatism, has clearly caused major impacts even on Bible scholarship. Bible scholars have been led to question the conservative timeline of the Bible.

Modern Bible scholars, for the most part, have become so conditioned to think in terms of the long ages of evolutionary geology that it never occurs to them that mankind once lived in the same world with the great animals that are now found only as fossils.[60]

R.K. Bentley tersely summarizes the major disparity: "*The standard evolutionary argument is that dinosaurs are separated from modern humans by a span of about 60 million years. If that were true, we could predict that no modern human has ever seen a dinosaur.*"[61]

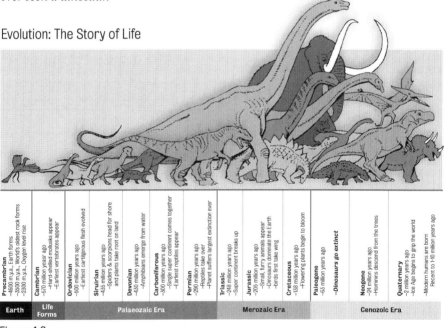

Figure 4.2

---

[60] Henry M. Morris, *The Remarkable Record of Job: The Ancient Wisdom, Scientific Accuracy, and Life-Changing Message of an Amazing Book* (Grand Rapids, Mich: Baker Book House, 1988), 115.

[61] R. K. Bentley, "Marco Polo Describes a Dinosaur," *A Sure Word*, 9 March 2012, https://rkbentley.blogspot.com/2012/03/marco-polo-describes-dinosaur_09.html.

As a result of this viewpoint, confident assertions abound claiming that dinosaurs and mankind cannot possibly have existed at the same time.

Let's illustrate. An article in the January 1993 publication of National Geographic boldly proclaimed: *"No human being has ever seen a live dinosaur."*[62] The indoctrination has even reached a level that American taxpayers subsidize. The United States Geological Survey asserts on their website: *"Did people and dinosaurs live at the same time? No! After the dinosaurs died out, nearly 65 million years passed before people appeared on Earth."*[63]

Confident assertions need to be backed up with hard facts or else houses will be built on sand. To borrow from the Apostle Paul, *"Therefore let him who thinks he stands take heed that he does not fall"* (1 Cor 10:12). Such pompous remarks make dismantling the system all the easier! Demonstration of even a single example would topple these houses; evolutionary scientists admit this! According to Louis Jacobs, professor at Southern Methodist University and former President of the Society of Vertebrate Paleontology,

> *Such an association [co-occurrence of men and dinosaurs] would dispel an Earth with vast antiquity. The entire history of creation, including the day of rest, could be accommodated in the seven biblical days of the Genesis myth. Evolution would be vanquished.*[64]

The late popular debater Ernst Mayr, out of Harvard University, remarked,

> *Creationists have stated that humans and dinosaurs were contemporaries in time . . . Were this momentous statement true the names of its discoverers would thunder down the corridors of time as individuals who made one of the most outstanding discoveries of the twentieth century.*[65]

Even the popular PBS program NOVA had a television special "God, Darwin, And the Dinosaurs" in which they pointed out that *"Finding [dinosaur footprints, side by side with humans] would counter evidence that humans evolved long after the dinosaurs became extinct and back up . . . [the] claim that all species, including man, were created at one time."*

---

[62] "The Age of the Dinosaurs," *National Geographic* 183[1] (1993): 142.

[63] United States Geological Survey, "Did People and dinosaurs live at the same time?, https://www.usgs.gov/faqs/did-people-and-dinosaurs-live-same-time?qt-news_science_products=0#qtnews_ science_products

[64] Louis L. Jacobs, *Quest for the African Dinosaurs* (New York: Villard Books, 1993), 261

[65] Gish-Mayr Debate, Evansville, Indiana.

Dismantling Babel's Tower[66]

Bold assertions are one thing, but evidence is another. Let's dismantle this common criticism of biblical creationists by considering some of the hard evidence at hand. We will do that by looking at historical testimony and artifacts from all six habitable continents. Even so, this list will of necessity be non-exhaustive. We encourage you to study further!

Coexistence Evidenced in Asia

Figure 4.3   Marco Polo

Marco Polo testifies of dinosaurs in his travels to China. He wrote about this experience and described what appears to many to be a Tyrannosaurus Rex. His testimony states,

Leaving the city of Yacho, and travelling ten days in a westerly direction, you reach the province of Karazan, which is also the name of its chief city . . . Here are seen huge serpents, ten paces in length, and ten spans in the girt of its body. At the fore part, near the head, they have two short legs, having three claws like those of a tiger with eyes larger than a fourpenny loaf (pane da quattro denari) and very glaring. The jaws are wide enough to swallow a man, the teeth are large and sharp, and their whole appearance is so formidable, that neither man, nor any kind of animal, can approach them without terror.

He further describes this beast saying,

By their motion in this way along the shore, and their vast weight, they make a deep depression, as if a heavy beam had been drawn along the sands. Those whose employment is to hunt them observe the track by which they are most frequently accustomed to go, and fix into the ground several pieces of wood armed with sharp iron spikes, which they cover with the sand in such a manner as not to be perceptible. When therefore the animals make their way towards the places they usually haunt, they are wounded by these instruments, and speedily killed.

---

[66] Several key sources for information in this section include Apologetics Press, Genesis Park, Steven Rudd and www.bible.ca, and http://www.truthaboutdinosaurs.org/.

Tangible artifacts from Asia abound. China boasts the famous Hongshan Jade Carvings, which clearly illustrate a Protoceratops. In the ancient Cambodian temple Ta Prohm near Angkor Wat there is a carving of what universally is recognized as a Stegosaurus. The temple dates to the twelfth century, a time well before moviegoers saw dinosaurs on the big screen. Artwork also attests to the Sumatran Crested Dinosaur (possibly Corythosaurus and Lambeosaurus or even a Velociraptor). And the Mesopotamian Cylinder Seal of Uruk in the Louvre (c. 3,300 BC) is yet another clear example of cohabitation of mankind and dinosaurs. What rational explanation explains their precision in depicting these creatures prior to the inception of organized paleontology, modern fossils, and media portrayals?

Coexistence Evidenced in Europe

Several ancient writers in Europe testify to the cohabitation of mankind and dinosaurs. Pliny the Elder wrote of massive serpentine creatures 120 feet long that could kill elephants and swallow stags and bulls whole. He draws a clear distinction between these and snakes, crocodiles, and other reptiles *(Natural History* VIII). Herodotus and Josephus describe creatures that fit the description of Pteranodons and Pterodactyls in their respective histories.

Figure 4.4 Pliny the Elder

In a 1983 expedition in Russia, paleontologists found human footprints alongside dinosaur footprints. The expedition and evidence were openly reported in *The Moscow News*. Remember the consequence of such a discovery according to the quote from the *NOVA* television program above?!

Anglican Bishop Richard Bell, who died in 1496, was buried in a tomb adorned with undeniable engravings of sauropods. In fact, one of the two sauropods bears a tail club with four spikes, a discovery which was unknown until 1989 from a *Shunosaurus* fossil found in China![67] The engravings are well attested to long before this discovery! Such beautiful gold engravings provide a goldmine of evidence for the biblical necessity of coexistence!

Figure 4.5 Herodotus

Italy boasts an embarrassment of riches in the dinosaur discussion. In the

---

[67] Z. Dong and D. Huang, "The Discovery of the Bony Tail Club of Sauropods," *Vertebrata PalAsiatica* 27.3: 219–224.

Figure 4.6 Shunosaurus fossil from China

pre-15th century Nile Mosaic of Palestrina, human warriors are depicted alongside dinosaurs. In the Hunt Mosaic from Pompeii (dating pre-79 AD) we see similar evidence. The Girifalco pottery sample which dates to pre-Greek times, attests to the coexistence of humans and the massive Stegosaurus.

Coexistence Evidenced in Africa And Australia

In Africa, we find more evidence. The West African nation of Mali boasts a bronze figurine of a hunter riding on the back of what clearly appears to be a Gryposaurus. Heading into central Africa to the jungle nation of Congo, we find consistent orally transmitted eyewitness testimony describing a creature living in the jungle swamps known as the Mokele-mbembe. Individual and independent eyewitness testimony has consistently agreed that a sauropod-like creature recently existed in this isolated part of the world. Whether or not this is currently the case, it is compelling enough to at least give passing consideration. Even if the eyewitnesses were merely passing on tribal traditions, it would still attest to coexistence of humans and sauropods; otherwise, how would these tribal peoples know how to describe these creatures?

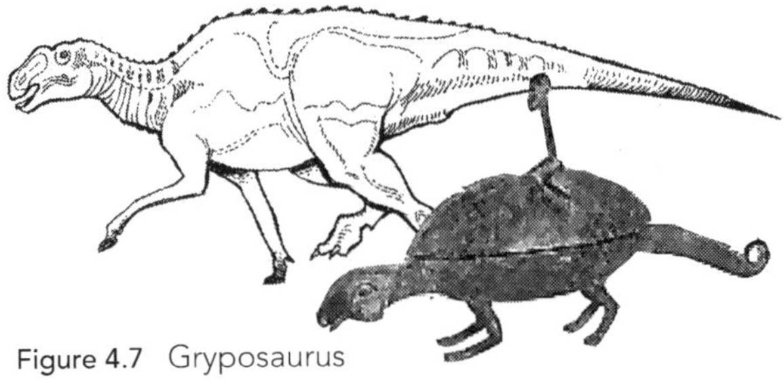

Australia offers similar evidence to what we find in Africa. Aboriginal tribesman from the seventeenth century provided consistent and independent description of a Plesiosaurus, which they called the "Yarru." Ab-

Figure 4.7 Gryposaurus

originals have also clearly described different animals fitting the description of other dinosaurs (known locally as the "Bunyip" and "Kultra"). Again, even if these individuals are not correctly representing what they themselves saw and are merely describing tribal traditions, it is inescapable that those traditions would be based in something of experience. The clarity of description suggests this can only reason-

---

[68] Samuel Hubbard, *Discoveries Relating to Prehistoric Man by the Doheny Scientific Expedition in the Hava Supai Canyon, Northern Arizona: With Supplement* (San Francisco: Sunset Press, 1924), 5.

ably find origin in experience with beasts similar to the description.

Coexistence Evidenced in North America

The Ancestral Puebloans (commonly referred to as the Anasazi Indians) lived in the Four Corners region of Utah, Arizona, New Mexico, and Colorado and thrived from 500-1300 AD. At one of their settlements at the Kachina Natural Bridge in Utah, these ancient peoples left a petroglyph of a sauropod next to a man. Similarly, there is a petroglyph of a Hadrosaur in Havaisupai Canyon in Arizona (discovered in 1879). The man who found this, Samuel Hubbard, says of the discovery,

> *The fact that some prehistoric man made a pictograph of a dinosaur on the walls of this canyon upsets completely all of our theories regarding the antiquity of man. Facts are stubborn and immutable things. If theories do not square with the facts then the theories must change, the facts remain.*[w]

Left, **Figure 4.8** the Burdick Track. Above, **Figure 4.9** Dinosaur art from Utah

Left, **Figure 4.10** Dinosaur art from the Grand Canyon. Above, **Figure 4.11** the Granby idol

Moving north into Granby, Colorado, we literally find rock-solid evidence for the coexistence of man and dinosaur. In 1920, farmer Bud Chalmers was clearing a field and noticed a large stone. Upon closer examination, the stone was noted to contain a carving of a mammoth, sauropod, and man and words from an ancient Chinese dialect dating back over a millennium.[69] The idol has since been misplaced, but three original, validated photographs taken by a schoolteacher preserve the truth of this artifact.

Moving much further north to the area of the Great Lakes, we find another testament to the coexistence of Native Americans and dinosaurs, this time with the Sioux in a cave in Ontario, Canada. These Native Americans clearly drew an Ankylosaurus with definite precision, enough to only reasonably be justified by eyewitness experience.

Coexistence Evidenced in Central and South America

Two massive collections in Central and South America overwhelmingly attest to coexistence of mankind and dinosaurs. These two collections are the Acambaro Figurines and the Ica Burial Stones of Peru.

The Acambaro collection was discovered in Acambaro, Mexico and consists of a collection of over 33,500 figurines and artifacts. Many of these are undeniably dinosaurs. The antiquity of these figurines, at least the vast majority of them, is attested to by other archaeological and paleontological findings in the area including the skeleton of a mammoth, teeth of an extinct horse, and human skulls. Steven Rudd summarizes some of the dating methods and findings that have taken place:

Figure 4.12 Ankylosaurus

Figure 4.13 Ica Stones

---

[69] The four words in English are North, River, Fruit, and Fish.

Figure 4.14 Acambaro dinosaur figurines

Figure 4.15 Peru dinosaur vase

In 1955 Charles Hapgood, respected Professor of Anthropology at the University of New Hampshire, conducted an elaborate investigation including extensive radiometric dating. He was accompanied by Earl Stanley Gardner, former District Attorney of the city of Los Angeles, California and the creator of Perry Mason. They falsified the claim that Julsrud manufactured the figurines, by excavating under the house of the Chief of Police, which was built 25 years before the Julsrud arrived in Mexico. Forty three more examples of the same type were found. Three radiocarbon tests were performed by Isotopes Incorporated of New Jersey resulting in dates of 1640 BC, 4530 BC and 1110 BC. Eighteen samples were subjected to thermoluminescent testing by the University of Pennsylvania, all of which gave dates of approximately 2500 BC. These results were subsequently withdrawn when it was learned that some of the samples were from dinosaurs.

He continues,

In 1990 an investigation was conducted by Neal Steedy, an independent archeologist who's [sic] livelihood depends on contract work from the Mexican government. He arbitrarily selected an excavation site considerably removed from the Julsrud site. Chards were found but no figurines. He commissioned radiocarbon tests for samples from the Julsrud Collection which produced a range of dates from 4000 to 1500 years ago. Then he decided to ignore the results because he claimed the figurines were too soft to last more than 20 years in the ground. He also ignored the fact that many of the acknowledged Chupicuaro pieces are of the same consistency and they survived just fine. Of course, some pieces in the Julsrud collection are beautifully fired. Steedy's effort does more to support Julsrud collection than to refute it. He effectively demonstrates the determination of the establishment to defend evolutionary dogma in the face of the devastating implications of this truly significant find.[70]

The Ica Burial Stones of Peru (typically dated 100 BC-1500 AD) are also an interesting and thought-provoking testimony to the coexistence of dinosaurs and mankind. While many are skeptical of these stones because ethically questionable non-professionals (known locally as *Huaqueros*) collected the massive and private Cabrera collection, it is important to acknowledge that many other Ica Burial stones have been dated by professionals to be of pre-Colombian descent and now reside in public museum collections for observation.[71]

Dinosaurs Mentioned in the Bible

General References

Critics of the Bible often reference that the Bible does not once use the term dinosaur. That's really not an issue as that term is a rather novel one dating to a mere century and a half ago. Synonymous terms are frequently used, most notably, "dragon." Also important to consider is the fact that all exhaustive Bible listings of animals necessarily include dinosaurs! A noteworthy example is found in Gen 1:20-25, which reads,

Then God said, "Let the waters teem with swarms of living creatures, and let birds fly above the earth in the open expanse of the heavens." God created the great sea monsters and every living creature that moves, with which the waters swarmed after their kind, and every winged bird after its kind; and God saw that it was good. God blessed them, saying, "Be fruitful and multiply, and fill the waters in the seas, and let birds multiply on the earth." There was evening and there was morning, a fifth day. Then God said, "Let the earth bring forth living creatures after their kind: cattle and creeping things and beasts of the earth after their kind"; and it was so. God made the beasts of the earth after their kind, and the cattle after their kind, and everything that creeps on the ground after its kind; and God saw that it was good.

---

[70] "The Dinosaur Figurines of Acambaro, Mexico," Bible.ca, http://www.bible.ca/tracks/tracks-acambaro.htm.

[71] For more discussion on these stones and how to determine their authenticity, see: "Can the Ica Stones Be Independently Verified?," *Journal of Creation* 30.3, (2016): 67-73.

Specific References: Behemoth

There are specific dinosaurs mentioned as well, although they are often over-looked. Job 40:15-24 identifies one such dinosaur named Behemoth. The text reads,

Behold now, Behemoth, which I made as well as you; he eats grass like an ox. Behold now, his strength in his loins and his power in the muscles of his belly. He bends his tail like a cedar; the sinews of his thighs are knit together. His bones are tubes of bronze; his limbs are like bars of iron. He is the first of the ways of God; let his maker bring near his sword. Surely the mountains bring him food, and all the beasts of the field play there. Under the lotus plants he lies down, in the covert of the reeds and the marsh. The lotus plants cover him with shade; the willows of the brook surround him. If a river rages, he is not alarmed; he is confident, though the Jordan rushes to his mouth. Can anyone capture him when he is on watch, with barbs can anyone pierce his nose?

Features of Behemoth (Job 40:15-24)	
Herbivore (v. 15)	Pre-Eminent (v. 19)
Massive (vv. 16-18, 23)	Spends Time in the Shade (vv. 21-22)
Incredible Strength (vv. 16-18)	Unafraid of Floods (v. 23)
Tail Like a Cedar Tree (v. 17)	Unable to Be Captured (v. 24)

Figure 4.16

So what does this text describe? This immediately sounds like a dinosaur, right? Particularly of the sauropod variety. Unfortunately, modern translations have cut themselves off at the feet by watering down this clear description with footnotes undermining Behemoth's identification as a dinosaur. The NASB and RSV ridiculously identify Behemoth as a Hippopotamus. Who in their right mind would describe a Hippopotamus as having a "tail like a cedar" (Job 40.17)? Hippos have tiny tails used to spread manure![72] Other translations like the NKJV and ESV timidly go more ambiguous with a footnote reading, *"A large animal, exact identity unknown."*

Numerous sauropod dinosaurs fit the description, namely "with a tail like a cedar." The Brachiosaurus measured 85 feet long. The Diplodocus was 90 feet long, and had a forty-five foot long tail that was made of double-beamed chevron bones on its underside. The Apatosaurus was 90 feet long with a tail comprised of eighty-two bones. The Argentinosaurus was seventy feet tall, weighed one hundred tons, was 120 feet long, and possessed a forty foot tail. The Supersaurus measured 138

---

[72] Hannelie Van As, "A hippo's tail," Getaway, https://www.getaway.co.za/wildlife/animal-stories/hippos-tail.

feet long and possessed a sixty foot tail. The most gargantuan of the sauropods was the Seismosaurus that measured 130-170 feet and possessed a kinked tail with wedge-shaped vertebra. Perhaps this is even alluded to by the Hebrew word in Job 40, which means "bent down."

Specific References: Leviathan

Immediately following this description of Behemoth, the inspired writer describes a creature called Leviathan.[73] Here's what God says in Job 41:

Can you draw out Leviathan with a fishhook? Or press down his tongue with a cord? Can you put a rope in his nose or pierce his jaw with a hook? Will he make many supplications to you, or will he speak to you soft words? Will he make a covenant with you? Will you take him for a servant forever? Will you play with him as with a bird, or will you bind him for your maidens? Will the traders bargain over him? Will they divide him among the merchants? Can you fill his skin with harpoons, or his head with fishing spears? Lay your hand on him; remember the battle; you will not do it again! Behold, your expectation is false; will you be laid low even at the sight of him? No one is so fierce that he dares to arouse him; who then is he that can stand before Me? Who has given to Me that I should repay him? Whatever is under the whole heaven is Mine. I will not keep silence concerning his limbs, or his mighty strength, or his orderly frame. Who can strip off his outer armor? Who can come within his double mail? Who can open the doors of his face? Around his teeth there is terror. His strong scales are his pride, shut up as with a tight seal. One is so near to another that no air can come between them. They are joined one to another; they clasp each other and cannot be separated. His sneezes flash forth light, and his eyes are like the eyelids of the morning. Out of his mouth go burning torches; sparks of fire leap forth. Out of his nostrils smoke goes forth as from a boiling pot and burning rushes. His breath kindles coals, and a flame goes forth from his mouth. In his neck lodges strength, and dismay leaps before him. The folds of his flesh are joined together, firm on him and immovable. His heart is as hard as a stone, even as hard as a lower millstone. When he raises himself up, the mighty fear; because of the crashing they are bewildered. The sword that reaches him cannot avail, nor the spear, the dart or the javelin. He regards iron as straw, bronze as rotten wood. The arrow cannot make him flee; slingstones are turned into stubble for him. Clubs are regarded as stubble; he laughs at the rattling of the javelin. His underparts are like sharp potsherds; he spreads out like a threshing sledge on the mire. He makes the depths boil like

---

[73] Other references to Leviathan include Job 3:8; Ps 74:14; 104:26; Isa 27:1.

a pot; he makes the sea like a jar of ointment. Behind him he makes a wake to shine; one would think the deep to be gray-haired. Nothing on earth is like him, one made without fear. He looks on everything that is high; he is king over all the sons of pride.

Leviathan's Features (Job 41)
Unable to Be Captured (vv. 1-6)
Terrifying (vv. 7-10, 14, 22, 25)
Armored And Scaly (vv. 7, 13, 15-17, 23-24, 26, 30)
Mightily Strong (vv. 12, 22, 27-29)
Large, Sharp Teeth (v. 14)
Breathes Fire (vv. 18-21)
Spends Time in Water (vv. 31-32)
Flies? Tenable Understanding, But Possible (v. 34)
Utterly Unique (v. 33)

Figure 4.17

Many have attempted to undermine this creature's identification as a dinosaur by dismissing the creature as mythological, but the first rule of biblical interpretation is if something can be taken literal, it should be. Christians should not allow intimidation from naturalistic scientists to cause them to forget this central rule. Furthermore, why would God actively and factually use mythology to demonstrate His power in the actual world? Would that not undermine His rhetorical strategy? And why would He use an entire chapter of the Bible to make this point? The key question is, can this entire chapter be understood factually. The answer is a resounding yes!

As with Behemoth, even modern Bible translations have been influenced by the propaganda likewise mishandling the identity of Leviathan. The NASB and RSV identify Leviathan as a Crocodile. The NKJV and ESV read, *"A large sea creature, exact identity unknown."* The biblical description here is clearly of a dragon. But that is just nonsense mythology, right? Not necessarily! There is an undeniable, ubiquitous, and ancient belief in dragons. Reason suggests the universality of belief is based in some truth of the past, much like the universal belief in the Flood of Noah is rooted in the historicity of Gen 6-9. But, could an animal actually breathe fire? All that would be needed biologically are a pocket of combustible gasses and bioelectricity, capabilities that are scientifically observed in numerous species (e.g. bombardier beetle or spitting cobra). The evidence is not prohibitive to the existence of dragons in antiquity.

What Happened to the Dinosaurs?

So, what happened to all the dinosaurs? After all, Behemoths and Leviathans seem to not exist anymore. Does the lack of these dinosaurs today have a sustainable and scientific explanation?

Two key ideas circulating for many years have been that dinosaurs and other creatures of antiquity went extinct as a result of asteroids/meteorites and ice ages. Belief in mass extinction by result of asteroid contact is based on formation study and other forms of geological research. For example, locations such as Chicxulub, Mexico, look to some scientists as a site of possible asteroid impact, but these postulations tend to be highly speculative and immensely problematic.[74] This hypothesis also begs the question. With such a massive contact, why would dinosaurs be the only creatures to go extinct? What about soft-skinned amphibians? Does it not stand to reason that they would go extinct before the thick skinned, scale-armored dinosaurs? In contrast to the precariousness of massive destruction by way of asteroid(s), ice ages seem undeniable given current evidence of creatures frozen in ice. To be clear, ice ages are not antagonistic to the biblical account; rather, they are quite likely given the worldwide Flood of Noah in which there would necessarily have been a super-cooling effect on the oceans of the world. Likely, post-Flood climate changes and fluctuations would have destroyed much of the dinosaur habitats.[75]

Evolutionists believe all of the animals that survived these possible causes of extinction proceeded to evolve into other forms. As we will see in future chapters, classic macroevolution has never been witnessed in scientific research and is no longer tenable given scientific advances. However, microevolution within kinds is something scientists have witnessed and this ability can explain some minor variation from antiquity. Examples across the board would include alligators, crocodiles, komodo dragons, and birds.

Common extinction is perhaps the most tenable explanation for the absence of ancient animal forms. Did you know that, currently, over two hundred species of flora and fauna go extinct every year? This rate continues at the same average each year, despite the well-intentioned efforts of preservation groups.[76] At this rate, in a period of a mere century, we have experienced the extinction of approximately twenty thousand species. That means that, if we assume this number as an average, according to the biblical timeline of six millennia, the Earth has seen the extinction of over 1.2 million species of flora and fauna. Likely, this rate was higher in the past. Given that there are only approximately fifty kinds of dinosaurs and the average size of a dinosaur was the size of an American bison,[77] it is not difficult to see how they could have gone out of existence. History, human nature, and common sense all suggest ancients eliminated more species they deemed threats to their existence.

Would you want a sauropod walking all over your village? Would you like a raptor hunting your children?

Conclusions Regarding the Dinosaur Discussion

Do dinosaurs matter for Christians? Yes! Absolutely! Writing off major elements of Earth history, undeniable life forms, or sticking one's fingers in his ears will not answer critics! In fact, these all-too-common responses actually feed criticisms of Christians, the Bible, and God. Disciples are explicitly commanded not to provide a ground of accusation for unbelievers (1 Pet 2:12; 3:15-16). This necessitates that we bone up on our studies and love God by defending His truths. There is no doubt, when we consult the copious available evidence, that mankind and dinosaurs existed at the same time. This fact vindicates the biblical record as trustworthy and accurate.

Any reflection on the Creation should result in our magnification of the Creator. His power and creativity are truly without end! Yet, as we strive to understand our Creator more through studies like these, we should be infinitely more impressed by His willingness to be stripped of His power and be born into this world. He gives the greatest display of His power and creativity in His life, death, burial, and resurrection. The One who made the dinosaurs willingly died to save you from your sins.

---

[74] For a well-rounded approach that provides a thorough critique of the Chicxulub impact hypothesis, see Timothy L. Clarey, "Do the Data Support a Large Meteorite Impact at Chicxulub?," Answers in Genesis, https://answersingenesis.org/dinosaurs/extinction/do-data-support-large-meteorite-impact-chicxulub.

[75] Tim Clarey, "Solving the Missing Tropical Dinosaurs Mystery?," Institute for Creation Research, https://www.icr.org/article/solving-missing-tropical-dinosaurs.

[76] This is not to say all such efforts are in vain or ineffective. Some are; some are not. Many factors determine effectiveness and many variables contribute to whether or not species will go extinct or not. In principle, the dominion mandate God gives at the beginning to mankind clearly implies a responsibility and accountability for what we do with and to the things of this world, including plants and animals.

[77] Timothy L. Clarey and Jeffrey P. Tomkins, "Determining Average Dinosaur Size Using the Most Recent Comprehensive Body Mass Data Set," *Answers Research Journal* 8 (2015): 85–91, https://assets.answersingenesis.org/doc/articles/pdf-versions/arj/v8/average-dinosaur-size.pdf.

Thought Questions:

1. Are dinosaurs friends or foes for Christians?

_____

_____

_____

_____

2. Did humans and dinosaurs coexist? How do we know this?

_____

_____

_____

_____

3. Differentiate between the study of artifacts and cryptozoology.

_____

_____

_____

_____

4. What Bible passages seem to discuss dinosaurs? What information do they give?

_____

_____

_____

_____

5. What happened to the dinosaurs?

_____

_____

_____

_____

CHAPTER 5

What Geology and the Fossil Record Do Not Show

Having brought into question the veracity of the naturalist's timeline by considering origins, the age of the Earth, and when the dinosaurs existed, we now consider another key area of evidence commonly offered for naturalism—the fossil record. Darwin grounded his ideas in the fossil record—a foundation that his peers said was unjustified. If the evidence is found wanting in the fossil record and Darwin's peers are shown to be correct in their skepticism, this would go a long way defensively to showing that belief in the God of the Bible is a reasonable conclusion. Before proceeding, let's take a moment to reiterate the importance of discussing such academic matters.

A Reminder of Just How Important These Studies Are

Is the winning of souls important to us? Is keeping loved ones in the faith important to us? Undoubtedly! If you had the opportunity to eliminate the biggest catalyst for rebellion to God, would you? If you had to learn some things that challenged you, would it be worth the effort? What if we told you that learning about the fossil record and what it did and did not show could both help people overcome obstacles to becoming Christians and help prevent your loved ones from falling away? Does this sound too good to be true?

M.D. and Ph.D. Biochemist Michael Denton writes, *"Chance and design are antithetical concepts and the decline in religious belief can probably be attributed more to the propagation and advocacy by the intellectual and scientific community of the Darwinian version of evolution than to any other single factor."*[78] Over the course of our next two chapters, we want to equip ourselves with the knowledge to counter this paralyzing effect of the advancement of naturalism, through the modality of macroevolution in particular, by taking a look at the fossil record. This study will stretch us, but it will also make us incredibly better at our role as Christians in our scientific apologetic.

We need to realize that evolution is not a benign theory and that engaging in this discussion is crucial for Christians. We do this to counter Satan's effective deception that differences between biblical creationism and macroevolution do not matter (cf. Col 2:4, 8). We perspicuously know that the Bible teaches mankind to use our senses to perceive and appreciate God through natural revelation. It stands

---

[78] Michael Denton, *Evolution: A Theory in Crisis* (London: Burnett, 1985), 66.

to reason then that our study of the Earth (Geology) and its fossils (Paleontology and Archaeology) would lead us to acknowledge Him. Sadly though, this conclusion has not always been drawn. So, let's look in this first chapter at what the fossil record does **NOT** show, knowing these matters will help Christians provide an accurate and informed critique of this number one factor in the decline in biblical theism.

A Few Important Terms to Know

King Solomon writes, *"Do not answer a fool according to his folly, or you will also be like him. Answer a fool as his folly deserves, that he not be wise in his own eyes."* (Prov 26:4f). The idea seems to be that different situations and different individuals require different responses.[79] In an effort to meet the macroevolutionist toe-to-toe, a discussion of technical verbiage is a good starting point. This will help pinpoint strongholds so that they may be torn down (2 Cor 10:3-5).

The Geologic Column

The Geologic Column is a hypothetical and tentative construct in which the layers of rock found on the Earth reveals an internationally recognized old-age timeline or history of the Earth. The Geologic Column is often considered scientific dogma. However, nowhere on Earth is the Geologic Column found like it is portrayed in textbooks. In fact, there are hundreds of locations where the order is totally different in the strata! Some fossil findings require scientists to reformulate entire chronological histories![80]

The Cambrian Fossil Layer (And Cambrian Explosion)

The Cambrian layer is one of the earliest life-bearing strata layers witnessed in geology. Since it is so early, if advanced life forms can be found in it (which they undoubtedly can) that would suggest that macroevolution does not satisfactorily

---

[79] Whether or not the person reveals himself to be naïve yet open minded, faithful, or foolish, determines where we go from this initial approach to meet him or her on his or her own level. Sometimes, one must dust his or her feet when faced with a fool who may be pounded in a mortar all day long, yet refuses to depart from his or her foolishness (Prov 27:22; Matt 10:14; Acts 13:51). Yet, even then, be confident that your labor has not been in vain (1 Cor 15:58), for God's Word will not return to Him without accomplishing the purpose for which He sent it out (Isa 55:11).

[80] One recent example is discussed in *University College London,* "New Dinosaur Found in the Wrong Place, at the Wrong Time," *ScienceDaily,* August 1, 2018.
"https://www.sciencedaily.com/releases/2018/08/180801182438.htm"

explain the origin of life. The "Cambrian Explosion" or "Cambrian Information Explosion" refers to the substantive and pronounced development of complex life that scientists do see in this layer of the fossil record.

Macroevolution vs. Microevolution

Macroevolution is the theory that all life forms on Earth possess common descent (I.e., everything including bacteria, plants, animals, etc. evolved from a single entity.). This is an unsubstantiated theory because not a single observation in a scientific setting has been observed. In fact, macroevolution could not be observed, as the timeline is prohibitive!

Microevolution, or adaptation, involves superficial changes within kinds based on environment and other influential factors. Superficial does not mean that they are not amazing, but that the fundamental body plan and genetics remain the same. This has been scientifically observed, most notably in fruit flies, moths, and certain bird species.

Transitional Forms

Transitional forms are fossils that are believed to illustrate macroevolution. These typically come in the form of bird fossils with supposed reptile features or reptile fossils with supposed bird features. However, other examples have been cited as well. Several examples of alleged transitional forms will be analyzed below including reptile-bird, Eohippus-to-horse, and ape-man transition.

Homology

Homology is the notion that similarity in different life forms proves macroevolution. This similarity may be in form, DNA, or other primary areas. An example of this is the classic argument that primate DNA and human DNA are exceptionally similar (an inaccurate and commonly misrepresented statistic), thus "proving" we are commonly descended.[81] Dr. Bo Kirkwood explains,

> *The genome, as we have seen, was mapped out for humans in 2003 and the chimpanzee in 2005. Originally, it was felt there was only a 1% difference in the DNA between the two kinds. In reality, there is a 6.4% difference. Is this a lot? Yes, and very much so . . . Curiously also, the genome for the Y chromo-*

---

[81] For a helpful examination of creation versus evolution in general, a critique of extrapolating from microevolution to macroevolution, and a critique of homology, reference: Bo Kirkwood, *The Evolution Delusion* (Athens, AL: Truth Books, 2016).

some in chimps has 37 genes and the human 78 genes. This is a 58% difference, not explained by traditional evolutionary processes, but would need some type of 'rapid' process. Also, telomeres (repeating sequences at the end of a sequence) are quite different with chimps having 23,000 and humans 10,000. Humans also have 687 genes chimps lack, and chimps have 86 genes humans lack. Where is the evolutionary explanation for this? Let's suppose apes and humans share considerable DNA. What does that prove? What separates humans from chimps is much more than mere DNA, as we have alluded to already.[82]

He goes on to explain these differences as including sentience, creative ability, moral code, desire for discovery, soul and spirit, and worship.[83]

The Fossil Record Does <u>NOT</u> Support Evolutionary Expectation And Timeline

"The first to plead his case seems right, until another comes and examines him" (Prov 18:17). There is perhaps no greater illustration of this than when the fossil record is examined without a priori acceptance of the macroevolutionary paradigm. Macroevolutionary scientists speak arrogantly, but they are springs without water and their worldview, in truth, enslaves (cf. 2 Pet 2:17-19).

The evolutionary timeline inherently requires titanic amounts of time and infinite transitional forms. This is because the system requires gradual, improving, and herculean change over copious amounts of time.[84] Charles Darwin ardently believed evidence for his theory was forthcoming and would be found in the fossil record. He believed transitional forms lay in situ, yet to be discovered. Niles Eldredge highlights this failed prediction:

He [Darwin, EP] prophesied that future generations of paleontologists would fill in these gaps by diligent search . . . It has become abundantly clear that the fossil record will not confirm this part of Darwin's predictions. Nor is the problem a miserably poor record. The fossil record simply shows that this prediction was wrong.[85]

---

[82] Bo Kirkwood, *Creation Versus Evolution* (Athens, AL: Truth Publications, 2017), 41-42.

[83] Dr. Jeffrey Tomkins has also pointed out the distinct differences between chimp and human genomes. His research has led to the conclusion that there is only an 80-85% human-chimp DNA similarity. Since macroevolution requires at least a 98.5% similarity, this is disastrous to the macroevolutionary paradigm. See his brief article and bibliography at http://www.icr.org/article/new-chimp-genome-confirms-creationistresearch.

[84] While the focus will be on Classical Darwinism, more modern theories such as Punctuated Equilibrium face many of the same criticisms and hang-ups.

Darwin's philosophical children lament the same incompleteness. However, the issue is not simply a matter of mere incompleteness, but rather selective incompleteness! There is a palpable absence of the transitional forms necessary to justify Darwin's theory. A world-renowned peer of Darwin's, Louis Agassiz, presented this criticism to him and Darwin admitted it was fatal to his theory.[86] In his personal correspondences, Darwin admits, *"If numerous species, belonging to the same genre or families, have really started into life at once, the fact would be fatal to the theory of descent with slow modification through natural selection."*

Figure 5.1   Louis Agassiz

Nevertheless, evolutionary scientists have futilely attempted to overcome this dearth of data. Their efforts have been creative but have not overcome the main issues. In these responses, evolutionists take numerous unjustified philosophical jumps extrapolating without basis from similarity to homology.[87] Highly imaginative leaps from a major lack of data are only bridged by colossal speculations.[88] One unmistakable illustration of this is seen in the extrapolation from fossil similarity between ape and man. Statistical breakdown of available fossils shows that 95% of the fossils we have are marine invertebrates, vertebrates are a small fraction of 1%, and primates are a tiny fraction of that! Despite this fact, many accept humans as being descendants of apes! Why? Worldview! Not evidence!

The Fossil Record Does <u>NOT</u> Show Transitional Forms in the Animal Kingdom

Let's consider some of these attempts to identify fossils as transitional forms. But before we look at specific examples, how appropriate at this juncture to con-

---

[85] Niles Eldredge and Ian Tattersall, The Myths of Human Evolution (New York: Columbia University Press, 1982), 45-46.

[86] For helpful discussion on this back and forth dialogue between Darwin and Agassiz, see Meyer, Stephen C. Meyer, Darwin's Doubt: The Explosive Origin of Animal Life and the Case for Intelligent Design (New York: HarperOne, 2014).

[87] The missing information in the nodes of branches on phylogenetic trees illustrates extrapolating without evidence.

[88] One author illustrates this, speaking of the australopithecines, in particular: "Nevertheless, because of the fossil gap, speculation has been rife for many years as to what gave rise to the australopithecines." Trevor Palmer, Controversy – Catastrophism & Evolution (Dordrecht: Kluwer Academic, 1999), 229.

sider a warning against erecting idols in our hearts.

> *"Present your case," the Lord says. "Bring forward your strong arguments," the King of Jacob says. Let them bring forth and declare to us what is going to take place; as for the former events, declare what they were, that we may consider them and know their outcome. Or announce to us what is coming; declare the things that are going to come afterward, that we may know that you are gods; indeed, do good or evil, that we may anxiously look about us and fear together. Behold, you are of no account, and your work amounts to nothing; he who chooses you is an abomination.* (Isa 41:21-24)

We most certainly need to be wary of idols bred from foolish and ignorant speculations (2 Tim 2:23). Having called to mind this warning, let's proceed.

Alleged Reptile-to-Bird "Missing Links"[89]

Archaeopteryx (i.e. "old wing")

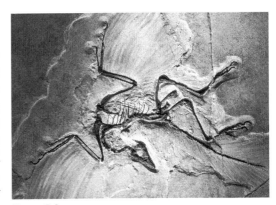

This fossil allegedly possesses "teeth" and "feathers," thus as an unmistakable transition from reptile to bird. However, scientists have repeatedly drawn out clear anatomical and genetic differences between reptiles and birds that cannot be explained. Dr. Bo Kirkwood concisely states:

Figure 5.2

> *Amongst evolutionists, Archaeopteryx is now felt to have evolved from a two-legged dinosaur, and as a result, paleontologists must now 'rearrange' the fossil's evidence to accommodate this since animals cannot be older than their ancestor! Archaeopteryx was in actuality a flying dinosaur and not a missing link, even though this is still perpetuated not only in textbooks but even in museums such as the Smithsonian.*[90]

---

[89] Dr. David Menton has a great discussion on key difficulties in explaining reptile to bird evolution in the Answers in Genesis DVD, *Formed to Fly.*

[90] Kirkwood, *Creation Versus Evolution,* 59.

Figure 5.3

Sinosauropteryx (i.e. "Chinese reptilian wing")

After further inspection, this fossil was revealed to be a theropod (i.e. small reptile), not a bird. The assumption that this was a bird resulted when scientists found filaments near a fossil and deceivingly labeled them "protofeathers." On further inspection, these filaments were revealed to be collagen fibers. Additionally, multiple bird samples were found in the same area of the Liaoning Province of China whose taxonomy is not undisputed, so if "Sinosauropteryx" was a precursor of birds, why are there actual fully-transitioned birds at the same time and place in the fossil record?

Archaeoraptor (i.e. "old robber")

Archaeoraptor was an infamous and universally recognized hoax in *National Geographic* that proves evolutionists will pay to get what they want to see. In this case, the fossil was clearly a combination of two totally separate forms! One scientist candidly admits, *"Though I do not want to believe it, Archaeoraptor appears to be composed of a dromaeosaur tail and a bird body."*[91] Oddly, many sources still cite Archaeoraptor as a real, substantiated transitional form!

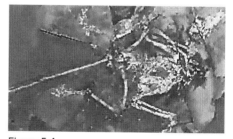

Figure 5.4

Sinornithosaurus (i.e. "Chinese bird reptile")

Sinornithosaurus is another "feathered dinosaur" based on Fossil NGMC 9 1. Scientists again found filamentous integumentary structures, which were thought to be wings, but have been proven to be connective tissue.

Storrs Olson, one of the world's foremost experts in avian paleontology, who also served as a curator of the Smithsonian Institute for many years, admitted in an open letter on November 1, 1999, that

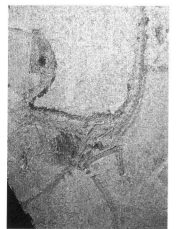

Figure 5.5

*The idea of feathered dinosaurs and the theropod origin of birds is being ac-
tively promoted by a cadre of zealous scientists acting in concert with certain
editors at Nature and National Geographic who themselves have become out-
spoken and highly biased proselytizers of the faith. Truth and careful scientific
weighing of evidence have been among the first casualties in their program,
which is now fast becoming one of the grander scientific hoaxes of our age.
There is not one undisputed example of a dinosaur with feathers. None. The
public deserves to know this.*[92]

The extrapolation of reptile-to-bird evolution of the sort discussed above is nothing more than sensationalistic, unsubstantiated, tabloid journalism. Yet, the examples cited above are commonly purported as scientific proof for macroevolution!

Alleged Evolution of the Horse from Eohippus

The Bible is clear that God intelligently and purposefully designed the horse in
the beginning. God describes His design of the horse:

*Do you give the horse his might? Do you clothe his neck with a mane? Do you
make him leap like the locust? His majestic snorting is terrible. He paws in the
valley, and rejoices in his strength; he goes out to meet the weapons. He laughs
at fear and is not dismayed; and he does not turn back from the sword. The
quiver rattles against him, the flashing spear and javelin. With shaking and
rage he races over the ground, and he does not stand still at the voice of the
trumpet. As often as the trumpet sounds he says, 'Aha!' and he scents the battle
from afar, and the thunder of the captains and the war cry* (Job 39:19-25).

In contrast, the typical evolutionary model will suggest that a very small four-
toed animal eventually changed into a much larger one-hoofed animal by a series
of intermediates. Do fossils support this? No! Darwinian evolution requires slow,
gradual change. If this had taken place we would expect one of the transitional
forms to possess two toes, yet not one has ever been found! Moreover, when we
look at the fossil record and examine the so-called transitional forms from Eohip-
pus to horse, we find one-hoofed horses in the same place as the three-hoofed.
In fact, in South America, we find the one-hoofed in lower strata than the three-
hoofed!

---

[91] Xu Xing, "Letter," *National Geographic* 197.3 (2000).

[92] Answers in Genesis has published a copy of this letter on their website.
https://answersingenesis.org/dinosaurs/feathers/sensationalistic-unsubstantiated-tabloid-jour-
nalism/

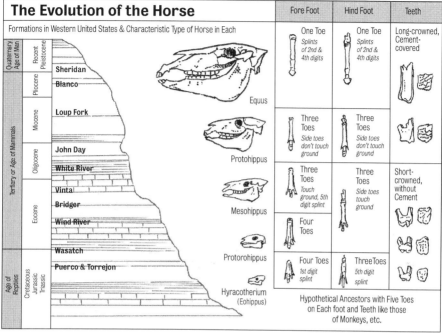

Figure 5.6   Alleged Horse Evolution

Another clear issue in the evolutionary model is the undeniable presence of genetic variation within the horse kind. Different animals can range in size within a species. Horses can vastly range in size. What we find in the fossil record is that each respective kind remains each respective kind. We see this in the horse kind (Eqquids) as well as other representative kinds such as the cat kind (Felids), dog kind (Canids), and bear kind (Ursids). There is variation (e.g. Shetland pony – Clydesdale; house cat – lion; Chihuahua – Great Dane; black bear – polar bear) but not outside of animal kinds.

The Fossil Record Does **NOT** Show Transitional Forms from Ape to Man

The Bible is clear in drawing a line of demarcation between man and animal. This is undeniable in Gen 1-2 where man is commanded to rule over the Earth and exercise dominion over every living thing. Gen 1:26-28 reads,

Then God said, "Let Us make man in Our image, according to Our likeness; and let them rule over the fish of the sea and over the birds of the sky and over the cattle and over all the earth, and over every creeping thing that creeps on the earth." God created man in His own image, in the image of God He created him; male and female He created them. God blessed them; and God said to

Figure 5.7
Human evolution

them, "*Be fruitful and multiply, and fill the earth, and subdue it; and rule over the fish of the sea and over the birds of the sky and over every living thing that moves on the earth.*"

This command is not given to apes. Another clear demarcation is made in Ps 8:4-5, which reads, "*What is man that You take thought of him, and the son of man that You care for him? Yet You have made him a little lower than God, and You crown him with glory and majesty!*" In the New Testament, we also see a powerful illustration of the difference in Jesus' clear view of the preeminence of man as illustrated in several of His prominent teachings (e.g. Matt 10:31; 12:12; Luke 13:10-17, etc.). Macroevolution does not recognize or value this difference. Mankind is reduced to a mere outgrowth of inconsequential and random processes with no destiny. He is a mere beast.

By far, the most commonly referenced illustration of macroevolution is that of ape-man. Following the paradigm of Dr. David Menton, we will examine and briefly critique the three typical ways to manipulate the fossil record to demonstrate ape-man transition.[93]

Method #1 – Upscaling Ape Fossils

The first way evolutionary scientists erroneously show ape-man transition is by upscaling apes in the fos-

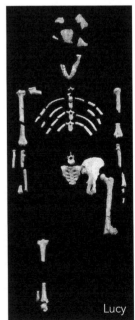

Lucy

Figure 5.8

---

[93] As illustrated in two of Dr. David Menton's videos with Answers In Genesis: *Lucy—She's No Lady!* and *Three Ways to Make an Ape Man.*

sil record. There is perhaps no greater illustration of this than Australopithecus afarensis, nicknamed "Lucy" after one sample, which found in Africa. For those unacquainted with Latin, Australopithecus simply means "southern ape," and afarensis simply means "from afar." The terminology is deceivingly simple.

The truth is that nearly all experts now agree this was a three-foot tall chimpanzee. Lucy's true identity as a chimpanzee is based on thorough scientific analysis of skull, hip, foot, and hand structures.[94] Researchers, even evolutionary ones (although they try and finagle out of the implications), have also proven that the famous Laetoli Footprints were not created by Lucy, but, rather, by humans.[95]

Despite this research, common lies and misrepresentations abound. A simple online search will reveal this to be the case when compared against reputable research. A notable and intentional misrepresentation is found in a past exhibit at the taxpayer-supported St. Louis Zoo. After purchasing a nearly twenty million dollar exhibit pompously asserting macroevolution as a fact, in which was a model of Lucy, scientists presented the data demonstrating Lucy's true identity as a chimpanzee. Directors admitted the facsimile misrepresented Lucy as a transitional form but refused to take the model down for the lifetime of the exhibit, citing that the overall representation of the exhibit was accurate![96]

Method #2 – Downscale Human Fossils

The second way evolutionary scientists erroneously show ape-man transition is by downscaling humans in the fossil record. Several examples may be considered.

Neanderthal man, as a stage in the development of humans from apes, is commonly used in texts and educational literature. Neanderthal man was revealed *six decades ago* at the International Conference of Zoology by Dr. A.J.E. Cave to be nothing

Figure 5.9 Neanderthal

---

[94] Two brief quotes will illustrate. "*A summary of the morphologic and functional affinities of the Hadar hand fossils leads inexorably to an image of a suspensory adapted hand, surprisingly similar to hands found in the small end of the pygmy chimpanzee-common chimpanzee range . . . There is no evidence that any extant primate has long, curved, heavily muscled hands and feet for any purpose other than to meet the demands of full or parttime arboreal life.*" J. Stern and R. Sussman, "The locomotor anatomy of Australopithecus afarensis," American Journal of Physical Antropology 60.3 (1983): 284, 308.

[95] R. H. Tuttle, 'Kinesiological inferences and evolutionary implications from Laetoli bipedal trails G-1, G-2/3 and A', Leakey and Harris, Ref. 1, Chapter 13.3, 503—523.

[96] Related in the St. Louis Dispatch, July 22, 1996, 1.

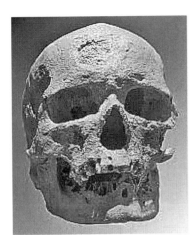

Figure 5.10 Cro Magnon

Figure 5.11 Heidelberg man

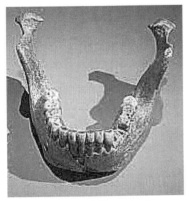

Figure 5.12 Heidelberg jawbone

more than an elderly modern man with arthritis! Another biology expert, Dr. David Menton, also examined the fossilized man and noted numerous broken bones (suggesting a rough life, which he postulates shows he existed briefly after the Flood) that had been set (indicating high intelligence). Also noteworthy is that in the same area and strata formalized burials, jewelry, tools, and flutes are witnessed.

Cro-Magnon Man is another commonly cited transitional form. This is one of the earliest and best-established fossils yet is equal in physique and brain capacity to modern man! So what's the difference?

Although not as cited, Heidelberg Man is another alleged transitional form, but analysis has revealed this missing link to be imaginatively built from a single jawbone of a modern human!

Method #3 – Combine Ape And Human Fossils, Or Just Make Stuff Up!

Let's consider two perfectly ridiculous examples of how commitment to macroevolution has caused tampering of the data. A total reconstruction of "Nebraska Man" was published in the *Illustrated London News* in 1922. Yet, "Nebraska Man" was built from a single tooth of an extinct pig! Piltdown Man was revered as proof for Darwinian evolution in a story entitled "Darwin Theory Is Proved True" on Sunday, December 22, 1912. However, "Piltdown Man" was built from the jawbone of a modern orangutan found in England! The actual scientific truth is clear: *"Despite the excited and optimistic claims that have been made by some paleontologists, no fossil hominid species can be established as our direct ancestor."*[97]

Figure 5.13 Nebraska man

Figure 5.14 Piltdown man

Consequences of Accepting Ape-Man Macroevolution

Let's return to how we began this section and explore the consequences of commitment to naturalism versus commitment to supernaturalism. To be clear, there is a substantive difference between animals and man.[98] Macroevolution denies this difference and strips mankind of his metaphysical and spiritual value. The late William Provine, the Charles A. Alexander Professor of Biological Sciences at the Department of Ecology and Evolutionary Biology at Cornell University states this clear effect of evolutionary biology:

> *There are no gods, no purposes, no goal-directed forces of any kind. There is no life after death. When I die, I am absolutely certain that I am going to be dead. That's the end for me. There is no ultimate foundation for ethics, no ultimate meaning to life, and no free will for humans, either.*[99]

You are less than nothing in the macroevolutionary paradigm. There is no practical difference between you and a monkey flinging its own feces. Are you ready and willing to accept that? That your loved ones are no different than cockroaches? Macroevolution confers no value on people and denies any spiritual essence whatsoever. I know you do not believe that! We know that, at root, no sound mind believes that!

---

[97] Richard Lewontin. Human Diversity (New York: Scientific American Library, 1982), 163.

[98] Travis Major, "Do Humans and Apes Differ Only by Degree?," Apologetics Press, http://apologeticspress.org/APPubPage.aspx?pub=1&issue=451&section=0&article=301&cat=328.

[99] William B Provine, "Darwinism: Science or Naturalistic Philosophy?," Origins Research 16 (1994): 9.

If you have accepted Darwinian Evolution, if mankind is merely a bacterium that just happened to spruce itself up over a couple billion years, then the Son of Man, Jesus Christ, was at least for a time, nothing but painted-up bacteria. Are you willing to gamble that?

One writer outlines well the two viewpoints and the choice before us:

Theories about the evolution of man describe a history of development taking many millions of years. It is a history filled with slow progression and countless deaths of ape-like creatures trying to evolve into the first human. This is a completely different history than the one recorded in the Bible in which Adam is formed from the dust as a fully-grown man, then Eve is formed from Adam's rib as a fully-grown woman. There is no way to reconcile these two histories.[100]

Another writer concurs:

There is no way to merge a less-than 10,000-years-old earth with a billions-of-years-old universe. There is no way to merge the instantaneous creation of Adam and Eve with the progressive evolution of thousands of hominids. There is no way to merge a perfect world without death with a world that includes millions of years of death . . . If certain things happened in the past, those things have inescapable consequences in the present.[101]

Concluding Thoughts

Mark Ridley, of Oxford University, states, *"No real evolutionist, whether gradualist or punctuationist, uses the fossil record as evidence in favor of the theory of evolution as opposed to special creation."*[102] Of course, other attempts are made to prop up the theory, but none have proven without critical and fatal issues. But the point is powerful—proof for macroevolution is not found in the fossil record! As Marvin Lubenow says, *"[Evolution] must be the only theory ever put forth in the history of science that claims to be scientific, but then explains why evidence for it cannot be found."*[103]

The Lord God Almighty created the world and everything in it in six literal days

---

[100] Del Tackett et al, *Is Genesis History?* (Nashville: Compass, 2017), 55.

[101] Thomas Purifoy Jr., "The Power of Alternate Histories of the Universe," Is Genesis History?, https://isgenesishistory.com/power-of-alternate-histories-of-universe.

[102] Mark Ridley, "Who Doubts Evolution?," New Scientist 90 (1981): 831.

[103] Mark Lubenow, *Bones of Contention: A Creationist Assessment of Human Fossils* (Grand Rapids: Baker Books, 2004), 334.

(Gen 1). He is incomprehensibly powerful and worthy of our highest adoration and worship (Rev 4:11). It is important that we give a case for faith even if that requires us to study areas beyond our normal scope. It is important because, if we fail to do so, we have contributed to the loss of souls. We need to prevent our children and loved ones from being taken captive by the blasphemous philosophy of Darwinian evolution! We need to refute this philosophy when our children ask us for answers! We need to challenge ourselves to grow in our knowledge!

Thought Questions:

1. How significant an impact has Darwinian evolution had on Christianity?

_____

_____

_____

_____

2. List some Bible passages that establish important principles in this discussion.

_____

_____

_____

_____

3. What is the difference between macroevolution and microevolution? Why is this distinction important?

_____

_____

_____

_____

4. What is the Cambrian explosion?

_____

_____

_____

_____

5. Pick one commonly cited example of evolution and research it more. Record some observations.

_____

_____

_____

_____

CHAPTER 6

What Geology and the Fossil Record Do Show

As we have seen in Chapters 2-5, how we view our origins makes a profound impact on our worldview and on our values. Either we come from a Creator or we are mere happenstance in a chaotic and pointless universe. Which viewpoint would you like to have?

The Bible tells us that mankind is the reflection of God's image (Gen 1:26-27), that we are incredibly valued and loved and that our lives have meaning and purpose. The Bible also affirms that we have a Grand Designer that is responsible for the incredible diversity and complexity of life on Earth. The number one worldview in opposition to this—the worldview taught in schools around the world, on vacations to landmarks and national parks, in textbooks, and in everywhere else you can imagine—is macroevolution, which wholly denies this identity and meaning. This worldview is dangerous, and it tears people away from God every single day. Consequently, the Christian's responsibility is to resist this onslaught of Satan by equipping himself or herself by the power of God to refute such distortions of knowledge.

And God assures empowerment in this epistemic enterprise:

Do not fear, for I am with you; do not anxiously look about you, for I am your God. I will strengthen you, surely I will help you, surely I will uphold you with My righteous right hand. Behold, all those who are angered at you will be shamed and dishonored; those who contend with you will be as nothing and will perish. You will seek those who quarrel with you, but will not find them, those who war with you will be as nothing and non-existent. For I am the Lord your God, who upholds your right hand, Who says to you, "Do not fear, I will help you" (Isa 41:10-13).

We need this power because it is the Christian's duty to give a reason for the hope within us (1 Pet 3:15), a hope which is built on the premise of God's existence and Jesus' identification with God and His proof in the resurrection.

In our previous chapter, we demonstrated that the fossil record—one key source of information about the world around us—does <u>NOT</u> upport the theory of macroevolution. In this demonstration we included that the fossil record does not support the evolutionary timeline and expectation and that alleged transitional forms (either between animals or humans) lack validity. This chapter will demonstrate what the record does in fact show.

Basic Facts in the Fossil Record

Top-Bottom Order And Disparity Preceding Diversity

Macroevolution would expect a bottom-top order in the fossil record; yet, the exact opposite, top-bottom order, is found! In effect what this produces is disparity preceding diversity, a real conundrum for macroevolutionists! So much so that classical evolution has been jettisoned by many scientists. Naturalistic scientists have desperately sought out another method to buttress evolution, but each method presented faces essentially the same issue. This is particularly seen in the proposed model of Punctuated Equilibrium, which posits that rapid shifts in morphology and taxonomy take place in isolated pockets of time and geography. Even this creative model fails to explain the roots of life in a massive eruption of disparity, as we will see in the next few sections.

When the Bible describes Creation, namely the creation of plants and animals, it specifies that God created life according to kinds. The Scriptures also specify that these life forms would reproduce according to their kinds (Gen 1:11-12, 21, 24-25). The Hebrew word for "kinds" in this passage is מין (pronounced "mean"). This is a broad term. The *Outline of Biblical Usage* explains,

> *Groups of living organisms belong in the same created 'kind' if they have descended from the same ancestral gene pool. This does not preclude new species because this represents a partitioning of the original gene pool. Information is lost or conserved—not gained. A new species could arise when a population is isolated and inbreeding occurs. By this definition a new species is not a new "kind" but a further partitioning of an existing "kind".*

To illustrate, examples of "kinds" that we can observe today would include: Ursids (Bears), Cannids (Dogs), Felids (Cats), Equuids (Horses). The variation among these original kinds is illustrated in different species that display different characteristics differentiating those species from other species, nonetheless existing within the same kinds (e.g. grey wolf versus Scottish terrier).

The Bible tells us that we start with several basic and very different "kinds" that diversify via species. This would suggest a top-down pattern and it is exactly what we see in the fossil record! Evolution would expect the opposite (i.e. all kinds from a single universal ancestor).

> *The course of appearance of taxa in the fossil record is top-down. What is more dramatic is that the number of phyla, which should increase by stages over long periods of time, actually decreases . . . Darwin's assumptions have been literally*

"overturned" in the fact of the fossil record, and paleontology has definitely and clearly invalidated his theory.[104]

In light of this evidence, how appropriate is the warning of Isa 45:9-10:

Woe to the one who quarrels with his Maker—An earthenware vessel among the vessels of earth! Will the clay say to the potter, "What are you doing?" Or the thing you are making say, "He has no hands"? Woe to him who says to a father, "What are you begetting?" Or to a woman, "To what are you giving birth?"

Explosive Origins of Information And Design[105]

The simple truth is that we see intricate body plans and genetic material unparalleled in complexity from the beginning. *"Lift up your eyes on high and see who has created these stars, the One who leads forth their host by number, He calls them all by name; because of the greatness of His might and the strength of His power, not one of them is missing"* (Isa 40:26). Eugene Koonin notes this from a scientific perspective,

The principal "types" seem to appear rapidly and fully equipped with the signature features of the respective new level of biological organization. No intermediate "grades" or intermediate forms between different types are detectable.[106]

Stephen C. Meyer further explains,

The animal forms that arose in the Cambrian not only did so without any clear material antecedent; they came on the scene complete with digital code, dynamically expressed integrated circuitry, and multi-layered, hierarchically organized information storage and processing systems.[107]

---

[104] Joseph Speckbach and Richard Gordon, *Divine Action and Natural Selection: Science, Faith and Evolution* (Singapore: World Scientific, 2009), 312.

[105] Several scientists have made effective use of this fact from the fossil record to dispatch evolution. See: Stephen C. Meyer, *Darwin's Doubt: The Explosive Origin of Animal Life and the Case for Intelligent Design* (New York: HarperOne, 2014). See also: *Darwin's Dilemma*, DVD, directed by Lad Allen (La Mirada, CA: Illustra Media, 2009).

[106] Eugene Koonin, "The Biological Big Bang Model for the Major Transitions in Evolution," *Biology Direct* 2.21 (2009).

[107] Meyer, *Darwin's Doubt*, 381.

Figure 6.1 Burgess Shale fossils

Two locations reveal extraordinary fossil beds especially illustrating this dilemma for Darwin: the Burgess Shale in British Columbia and the Maotianshan Shale near Chengjiang, China.

Discontinuity And Stasis[108]

Yet another key issue for evolutionists is the clear and numerous examples of discontinuity and stasis in the fossil record. For those unacquainted with such terms, this essentially means that animals exist with a certain form, then go extinct or are extant in the same form with no intermediate transitions found.

Notorious evolutionist Richard Dawkins confesses this difficulty (and he even admits how it aids the apologetic of creationists!):

It is as though they [fossils] were just planted there, without any evolutionary history. Needless to say, this appearance of sudden planting has delighted creationists . . . Both schools of thought (Punctuationists and Gradualists) despise so-called scientific creationists equally, and both agree that the major gaps are real, that they are true imperfections in the fossil record. The only alternative explanation of the sudden appearance of so many complex animal types in the Cambrian era is divine creation and (we) both reject this alternative.[109]

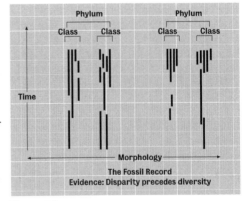

Figure 6.2

Scientific creationist Stephen C. Meyer notes how intelligent design (as we are contending, biblical creationism) serves well to explain the problem:

Intelligent design also explains the observed stasis in the fossil record . . . Cambrian species tend to persist unchanged in their basic forms over time. Animal body plans that define the higher taxa, including classes and phyla, also remain especially stable in their basic architectural design, showing 'no directional change' over geological history after their first appearance in the Cambrian. As a result, the morphological disparity between distinct animal body plans remains unbridged.[110]

Soft-Tissue Preservation

A great testament to the biblical paradigm is the ever-increasing cornucopia of fossils exhibiting soft-tissue preservation. Several examples include: the nearly intact Hadrosaur (nicknamed "Dakota") discovered in 1999, the duck-billed dinosaur (nicknamed "Leonardo") found in 2000 (with 90% of its skeleton covered in soft tissue), the Nodosaur (nicknamed the "four-legged tank") found in 2011 (which is commonly referred to as the best preserved fossil of its kind), the slew of mammoths found ranging from Mexico to Russia (e.g. "Yuka"), ad infinitum. Let's dig into a few examples more specifically.

In 2000, Bob Harmon and a team of paleontologists uncovered the skeleton of an adolescent T. Rex (nicknamed "B. Rex" in his honor). In order to transport it, the skeleton was broken apart. One of the teams, led by Mary Higby Schweitzer, broke the thighbone and examined the inside of it. Inside of this dinosaur bone were blood vessels, cells, and developmental protein matrix! Rarely do these survive one thousand years, let alone sixtyfive million years! What they found has rocked the scientific community![111]

In 2012, Microbiologist Kevin Anderson and Mark Armitage, M.S., Ed.S., uncovered a four-foot long triceratops horridus brow horn at the Hell Creek Forma-

---

[108] A perfect illustration of stasis throughout the fossil record is seen in the still extant horseshoe crab, which is found in the Cambrian layer with precisely the same form observed today.

[109] Richard Dawkins, *The Blind Watchmaker: Why the Evidence of Evolution Reveals a Universe Without a Design* (New York: W.W. Norton, 1996), 229-230.

[110] Stephen C. Meyer, Darwin's Doubt, 377.

[111] Mary H. Schweitzer, et al., "Soft-tissue Vessels and Cellular Preservation in Tyrannosaurus Rex." Science 307.5717 (2005): 1952; Mary H. Schweitzer, *Microstructural, Elemental and Biomolecular Preservation of Tyrannosaurus Rex Cancellous Tissues*. 1995; Mary H. Schweitzer, et al., "Analyses of Soft Tissue from Tyrannosaurus Rex Suggest the Presence of Protein." Science. 316.5822 (2007): 277-280; M. Higby Schweitzer and John R. Horner. "Intravascular Microstructures in Trabecular Bone Tissues of Tyrannosaurus Rex." *Annales De Paléontologie*. 85.3 (1999): 179-192; J.M. Asara, et al., "Protein Sequences from Mastodon and Tyrannosaurus Rex Revealed by Mass Spectrometry." Science. 316.5822 (2007): 280-285.

Figure 6.3 Four-legged tank

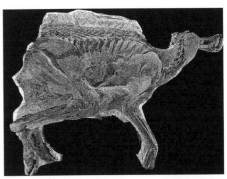

Figure 6.4 Duck-billed dinosaur, "Leonardo"

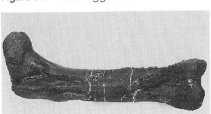

Figure 6.5 B-rex thighbone

Figure 6.6 Triceratops horn

tion in Montana. Upon analysis under a dissection microscope at first, and later a scanning electron microscope in Northridge, California, they noted preserved tissues and cells and possibly even proteins like collagen. This, again, begs the question, how is that preserved?! Especially at Hell Creek with extreme temperature shifts each year. Temperature changes and other forces of decomposition destroy these types of tissue.

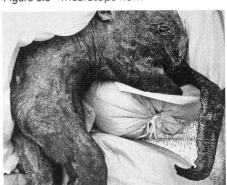

Figure 6.7 Wooly mammoth found in Siberia

But haven't scientists objectively proven the time needed for fossilization to occur? No! Did you know that scientists have recently shown that fossilization can take place in a mere twenty-four hours under the right circumstance (namely, heat and pressure intense enough, but not too intense so as to destroy the fossil).[112] The classic example of this is of a fossilized hammer found in strata incorrectly dated to be over 140 million years old![113] The hammer is clearly not that old, so nei-

---

[112] Evan T. Saitta, et al., "Sediment-encased Maturation: a Novel Method for Simulating Diagenesis in Organic Fossil Preservation," https://onlinelibrary.wiley.com/doi/full/10.1111/pala.12386 .

[113] Steven Rudd, "Fossilized Hammer," http://www.bible.ca/tracks/fossilized-hammer.htm

ther is the formation. Without blindly accepting naturalistic presuppositions, it's amazing what science reveals!

Given the naturalistic-evolutionary timeline, these findings are utterly inconceivable! So, what is the solution? Is there a solution? Certainly there is— these findings validate the Bible's timeline of history!

Figure 6.8 Fossilized hammer

Variation And Adaptive Ability within Kinds

Earlier, we explained that the creation account in Genesis speaks of God's establishment of representative kinds (cf. Gen 1:11-12, 21, 24-25). This reality practically serves to explain Adam's ability to name the animals on a single day. Likely also would be that Noah was only required to have representative kinds on the ark, which would provide more than enough room to accommodate kinds as opposed to each individual species. We see many of these kinds today, as they serve as the basis for taxonomical systems, imperfect though these systems are.[114]

Far from disproving biblical creationism, variation and adaptation are undeniably taught in the Scriptures. A key passage where this is made evident is Acts 17:24-31, which states,

The God who made the world and all things in it, since He is Lord of heaven and earth, does not dwell in temples made with hands; nor is He served by human hands, as though He needed anything, since He Himself gives to all people life and breath and all things; and He made from one man every nation of mankind to live on all the face of the earth, having determined their appointed times and the boundaries of their habitation, that they would seek God, if perhaps they might grope for Him and find Him, though He is not far from each one of us; for in Him we live and move and exist, as even some of your own poets have said, "For we also are His children." Being then the children of God, we ought not to think that the Divine Nature is like gold or silver or stone, an image formed by the art and thought of man. Therefore having overlooked the times of ignorance, God is now declaring to men that all people everywhere should repent, because He has fixed a day in which He will judge the world in

---

[114] For an interesting and thought-provoking alternative to current taxonomical systems, see: Alan Herberger, "Organizing Creation: The Science of Created Kinds," *Orchard of Life Science*, http://orchardoflifescience.com/2018/08/22/organizing-creation-the-science-of-created-kinds-2/.

righteousness through a Man whom He has appointed, having furnished proof to all men by raising Him from the dead.

Figure 6.9

Science has witnessed and testified to this variation, although naturalistic worldviews have often muddied the true effect of these examples. Several examples serve to illustrate.

No doubt, a key icon of evolution has been the finch of the Galapagos Islands. Ironically, though Darwin studied the finches on the Galapagos Islands, he does not speak of them in his infamous work *On the Origin of Species*! They only became icons years later by those with allegiance to materialism. Creationists cannot and should not deny the variation seen in the finch population in the Galapagos. There is no doubt that variation is present in the finch kind, especially in the Galapagos Islands, but this merely illustrates adaptation! This clearly does not serve to prove infinite, exponential, and advantageous growth from primordial goo to modern man!

Another key icon has become the peppered moths of England. Bernard Kettlewell in Birmingham, England, was one of the first to study these fascinating creatures. He noticed two main variations of color within the species. One was a very light color and the other was a very dark color. Evolutionists often cite these moths as proof of macroevolution. They claim the darker version was able to thrive more because they could blend into darker birch trees, thus hiding from predatory birds. Interestingly, pictures are often staged with moths being pinned onto birch tree bark to prop up this hypothesis. In actuality, these moths typically do not rest on the bark, but rather on the underside of its leaves! Furthermore, if this really is why the darker moths became more prevalent, which is itself suspect, this shows adaptation, not macroevolution!

Figure 6.10 Finches of the Galapagos islands

Figure 6.11 Peppered moth

Of course, nobody really cares about the evolution of moths and finches; the real crux of the matter is in humans—did apes evolve into man? Certainly not! However, we do see vast amounts of variation in humans and that does deserve explanation. Anthropologists witness variability every time they study human skulls. Pronounced differences exist between Aboriginals, Inuit, Masai warriors, and other cultures found in different locations. A single family in any given location may possess giant-like members and dwarfish members. Truly, this variation is not an issue for biblical creation, which not only assumes variation, but also identifies the One Who designed this variation! Again, variation is not equivalent to macroevolution; variation should never be misconstrued as macroevolution.[115]

While variation is seen in a plethora of examples, variation has limits. As incredible as variations can be, they are constrained. Developmental mechanisms restrict the degree to which organisms may vary without deleterious consequences.[116]

Does Show Evidence For a Global Catastrophic Flood[117]

Noah's Flood

In Gen 6-8, the Bible relates an event that could not help but go unnoticed in scientific inquiry, even today.[118] The Lord tells Noah that He plans to flood the entire Earth due to the widespread depravity of man. In His infinite grace, He provides Noah and his family with a plan that will preserve them through this global catastrophe. Noah spends many years with his sons faithfully building an ark of gopher wood just as God had instructed. The ark is then filled with a pair of all animals on Earth (seven for the clean animals to furnish a sacrifice after the flood is over—7:2-3) as well as food and provisions. All of these animals board the ark with Noah's family after they load it with supplies and the door is sealed. The fountains of the great deep burst forth (7:11) and the windows of the heavens unleash a flood unparalleled in the history of man. According to the Bible, this is the first rain upon

---

[115] Variation and microevolution is also seen in antibiotic-resistant bacteria such as MRSA. But, again, it is still bacteria!

[116] For in-depth examination of these limitations and how they produce problems for macroevolution, see Meyer, Darwin's Doubt, 155-287; Michael J. Behe, *Darwin's Black Box: The Biochemical Challenge to Evolution* (New York: Free Press, 2006).

[117] The information in this section is due in large part to the efforts of Steve Austin, Andrew Snelling, and other Bible-believing geologists who have made leaps and bounds in this field. *Is Genesis History?* Contains brief interviews with both of these scientists and the various educational tools of *Answers in Genesis* are saturated with their work. See: https://answersingenesis.org/the-flood/. Do not fail to look into these sources more!

the Earth, and what a rain it is! The rain prevails for forty days and nights, and the family spends months and months upon the ark until the waters recede, and the ark rests upon a mountain of Ararat. Later in the Hebrew canon, we find this further description of the Flood:

> *He established the earth upon its foundations, so that it will not totter forever and ever. You covered it with the deep as with a garment; the waters were standing above the mountains. At Your rebuke they fled, at the sound of Your thunder they hurried away. The mountains rose; the valleys sank down to the place which You established for them. You set a boundary that they may not pass over, so that they will not return to cover the earth.* (Psa 104:5-9)

If this indeed happened, geologists and other scientists should possess mountains of evidence. The fact is, this is exactly the case! For many years, naturalists and atheists wholeheartedly doubted the possibility of a global flood.[119] Recent research renders that conclusion totally obsolete. Of course, stubbornness knows no end, and now naturalists hypothesize a succession of sweeping floods that allegedly explains the undeniable evidence. Using the principle of competing hypotheses, we see that the biblical Flood measures up to the evidence while the naturalistic hypothesis does not.

Rapid Deposition of Sedimentary Layers

Certainly the great general testimony to Noah's Flood is the observed widespread historical fact of rapid destruction and deposition. This we would expect from a global deluge of Noah's magnitude, but not of the proposed ebb and flow type floods suggested by naturalistic scientists. Dr. Bo Kirkwood explains:

> *The flood was an event of supreme uniqueness, and nothing like it has ever been witnessed since. The worldwide flood of Noah's day would have significantly changed the topography and geology of the world as it was known then*

---

[118] There is an extraordinary extended chiasmus (or palistrophe) present in the Flood pericope of Genesis. Fifteen points are presented and then inverted with the crux being that "God remembered Noah."

[119] *"Know this first of all, that in the last days mockers will come with their mocking, following after their own lusts, and saying, 'Where is the promise of His coming? For ever since the fathers fell asleep, all continues just as it was from the beginning of creation.' For when they maintain this, it escapes their notice that by the word of God the heavens existed long ago and the earth was formed out of water and by water, through which the world at that time was destroyed, being flooded with water. But by His word the present heavens and earth are being reserved for fire, kept for the day of judgment and destruction of ungodly men"* (2 Pet 3:3-7).

and may be responsible for many of the formations we see today.[120]

Scientists have indeed unveiled rapidly established sedimentary layers across continents such as the Coconino sandstone, red sandstone, and chalk beds across North America. Many of these layers are seen elsewhere in the world, suggestive of long transport of sediments.[121] These sedimentary layers possess rapidly established knife-edge erosional boundaries, perhaps the greatest of which is the Great Un-conformity witnessed at the Grand Canyon. These formations also at times hold bent and folded strata. Many of these layers also possess waving patterns that scientists such as John Whitmore, Andrew Snelling, Paul Garner, and Steve Austin show to be caused by underwater sand erosion.[122]

Figure 6.12   The Great Unconformity

Figure 6.13   The Grand Canyon

Rapid Deposition of Plants And Animals

Geologists and archaeologists clearly see the rapid deposition of plants and animals in evidences such as polystrate fossils, fossil beds with graded bones, and the pure survival of such a massive amount of fossils. Polystrate fossils vertically extend

---

[120] Bo Kirkwood, *Creation Versus Evolution* (Athens, AL: Truth Publications, 2017), 52.

[121] Another helpful illustration of this is when a massive salt formation borders a massive sandstone formation such as in the U.S. Gulf Coast region where the Upper Jurassic Norphlet Sandstone rests on top of thousands of feet of the Middle Jurassic Louann Salt. Tim Clarey again is helpful here when he notes, *"The Norphlet is another case where uniformitarian geology fails. Blanket sands are best explained as massive Flood deposits as the waters advanced and/or retreated. The Norphlet appears to be a mid-Flood deposit nead<-Is this spelled correctly? the base of the Zuni Megasequence. Rapid shifts in rock types (i.e., from salt to sandstone) are best explained by sudden shifts in direction of tsunami-like waves, bringing in sediment from different locations and sources during the Flood."* (Tim Clarey, "More Whopper Sand Evidence of Global Flood," Institute for Creation Research, http://www.icr.org/article/more-whopper-sand).

[122] Andrew Snelling, et al., *Set in Stone: Evidence for Earth's Catastrophic Past* (Irvine, Calif: Randolf Productions Inc., 2012).

across assumed time boundaries in the strata. Graded bones in fossil beds suggest rapid deposition of the sort most reasonably produced by something like Noah's Flood.[123] Fossil beds have also produced massive coal beds and fossil fuel deposits best explained by the biblical Flood. Additionally, just considering that the preservation of fossils is very difficult—e.g. weather, animals, erosion—necessitates rapid burial to explain the vast fossil beds we find preserved to the degree in which they are preserved.

Figure 6.14 Polystrate fossils

What is particularly fascinating about the animals found in the fossil record is also the nature of what is found. The first layer of animals in the fossil record is composed of shallow water invertebrate fossils. The second layer is composed of amphibians. The third layer is composed of reptiles. Successive layers contain mammals and birds. Far from demonstrating the viability of macroevolution, as the story normally is spun, these layers show evidence of a global flood. Why? Because the Flood of Noah began in the world's ocean basins (cf. Gen 7:11) with the ocean floor ripping apart, creating tsunamis that would have deposited shallow water invertebrates onto continents first, then suffocated fish, then amphibians, then reptiles, mammals, and birds. Scientists even see footprints of these animals futilely trying to escape the Flood; naturalists, because of presuppositions, allege the footprints and animals who made them are separated by thousands or millions of years! Notably, this order is not just true of animals, but also of habitats! Noah's Flood also reasonably explains examples of the long transport of animals over continents, up mountains, and across deserts.[124]

---

[123] Tim Clarey, Ph.D. has a helpful article demonstrating young earth creationism and the validity of Noah's Flood as the agent of major fossil beds by looking at evidence from the Morrison Formation. See: Tim Clarey, "Dinosaurs Buried More Rapidly Than Thought," *Institute for Creation Research*, http://www.icr.org/article/dinosaurs-buried-more-rapidly-than-thought.

[124] The Institute for Creation Research (ICR) is currently developing a biblical paleo-biogeography model that will prove most helpful in explaining this transport. See: Jeffrey P. Tomkins and Tim Clarey, *Institute for Creation Research*, http://www.icr.org/article/building-biblical-paleo-biogeography-model.

Concluding Thoughts

When you ask the right questions, you get the right answers! In this book we confidently believe that we have been asking the right, challenging questions in the field of science. And what is the reasonable conclusion? The Bible is reliable, God does exist, and the history of our world shows an origin that confers importance and value on us.

The fossil record is a tool available to us to provide evidence for belief in God. In no way does it demonstrate the validity of macroevolution; rather, it unequivocally agrees with the Bible. As ancient Judah was warned of relying on useless idols, we give the same warning to those who reject God for the idol of naturalism:

> *As the thief is shamed when he is discovered, so the house of Israel is shamed; they, their kings, their princes and their priests and their prophets, who say to a tree, "You are my father," and to a stone, "You gave me birth." For they have turned their back to Me, and not their face; but in the time of their trouble they will say, "Arise and save us." But where are your gods which you made for yourself? Let them arise, if they can save you in the time of your trouble; for according to the number of your cities are your gods, O Judah* (Jer 2:26-28).

And as the Apostle Paul admonishes the Romans, *"Let God be found true, though every man be found a liar, as it is written, 'That You may be justified in Your words, and prevail when You are judged'"* (Rom 3:4).

Thought Questions:

1. What sort of order do we see in the fossil record? What order would Darwinian evolution expect?

_____

_____

_____

_____

2. What is stasis and what credence does it give to the biblical paradigm?

_____

_____

_____

_____

3. What is variation? Does the Bible speak of it?

_____

_____

_____

_____

4. What role does the global flood of Genesis 6-8 play in this discussion?

_____

_____

_____

_____

5. Of what does the Grand Canyon testify?

_____

_____

_____

_____

CHAPTER 7

An Introduction
to Intelligent Design

In Chapter 1, we reviewed the war going on between Satan and God's people, a war that occurs in major ways in the scientific domain. In Chapter 2, we discussed a classic approach for the existence of God known as the Cosmological Argument. Rather straightforward, this method of reasoning suggests that there is an Unmoved Mover or an Uncaused Cause. In Chapters 3-6 we dealt with issues, questions, and subjects primarily related to the historical sciences that are outgrowths of the dichotomy of naturalistic and supernaturalistic cosmology.

Another key approach for the existence of God is known historically as Natural Theology (i.e. reasoning from nature that there is a God). This tactic can be more specifically narrowed into what is known as the Teleological Argument (Greek: *teleos* – perfect; orderly; completeness; design). Most often, when the teleological argument is being used nowadays, it is in reference to Intelligent Design (ID). This concept is again antithetical to and distinct from the theory of Naturalism, which contends that life originated without oversight or design.

While philosophical in premise, scientific evidence in support of ID is abundant. Additionally, it is biblical.[125] In fact, the writer of Hebrews makes an argument from ID by saying, *"Every house has a builder; the Builder of all things is God"* (Heb 3:4). So when we refer to ID, we are scientifically exploring what the inspired writer of Hebrews means with this statement.[126] So, let's explore!

Concepts at the Root of ID

Looking in the scientific literature, one will find several key terms and ideas that form the basis of ID. These four ideas are the design's signature, irreducible complexity, specified complexity, and fine-tuning. Biblically, God's rebuke of Job in chapters 38-41 seems to generally imply each of these foundational ideas.

---

[125] To be clear, not all advocates of ID are espousing Christians, nor is it necessary to be a Christian to argue for ID. Dr. Georgia Purdom has a brief, helpful examination of why the two are not equivalent in *The New Answers* DVD 2.

[126] Compare other verses like John 1:3; Isa 48:13; Ps 139:14-15; Gen 1; Pss 8; 19; 33:6-9; and Rom 1:20.

The Signature of Design (aka fingerprints of a designer)

The "signature" or "look" of design is attested to in many examples ranging from simple complexity (e.g. a sheet of paper) to incredible complexity (e.g. the Large Hadron Collider). Even in examples of simple complexity, the trademark is still readily apparent. Considering our example above, a piece of paper is not particularly difficult to make, yet it still points to a maker after production. Why is this? It conveys design by its nature.

Our world is considerably more complex than a sheet of paper. There are systems, objects, beings, and a billion other realities that convey information, purpose, and production. ID takes this all back to its cosmological root.

Scientists do study and acknowledge

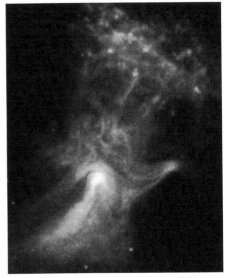

Figure 7.1 Hand of God Pulsar Wind Nebula

this sort of look, but one does not need to be a scientist to appreciate the concept. Non-scientists do this in everyday life and we take it for granted; the signature of design is a commonly accepted deduction. If we see a house, we reason that someone built it, even if we did not witness its being built (cf. Heb 3:4). It is completely irrational to believe otherwise. This concept may likely be what Paul has in mind when he writes in Rom 1:18-25,

> *For the wrath of God is revealed from heaven against all ungodliness and un-righteousness of men who suppress the truth in unrighteousness, because that which is known about God is evident within them; for God made it evident to them. For since the creation of the world His invisible attributes, His eternal power and divine nature, have been clearly seen, being understood through what has been made, so that they are without excuse. For even though they knew God, they did not honor Him as God or give thanks, but they became futile in their speculations, and their foolish heart was darkened. Professing to be wise, they became fools, and exchanged the glory of the incorruptible God for an image in the form of corruptible man and of birds and four-footed animals and crawling creatures. Therefore God gave them over in the lusts of their hearts to impurity, so that their bodies would be dishonored among them. For they exchanged the truth of God for a lie, and worshiped and served the creature rather than the Creator, who is blessed forever. Amen.*

Irreducible Complexity

Biochemist Michael Behe defines irreducible complexity as "a single system composed of several well-matched, interacting parts that contribute to the basic function,

Figure 7.2

wherein the removal of any one of the parts causes the system to effectively cease functioning."[127] The classic example cited is of a traditional mousetrap, where the removal of any constituent element destroys function.

Historically, Behe and other more recent scientists have more fully developed this idea; however, the idea of irreducible complexity is not original to them. French scientist Gustav Cuvier describes the same idea over 150 years prior:

> Every organized being forms a whole, a unique, and perfect system, the parts of which mutually correspond, and concur in the same definitive action by a reciprocal reaction. None of these parts can change without the whole changing; and consequently each of them, separately considered, points out and marks all the others.[128]

Specified Complexity

Information scientists have added onto the idea of complexity by developing and citing examples of what is identified as specified complexity. These scientists correctly point out that simple randomness is complex by definition and unlikely by default. However, they are quick to point out that what is observed is not simply random or improbable; what is seen in natural systems is engineering for purpose, even communication specifically (an aspect we will discuss more thoroughly in Chapter 10 on information). Parts, pieces, and components are not only existent and developed, but they serve a very precise purpose, and, without everything being "just-so," that purpose could not be served. Mathematician A. Cressy Morrison wanted to put a figure to the likelihood of this happening. He calculated that the chances of what we observe in nature occurring are 1 in 1×10^{340} million.[129]

A few examples serve to illustrate. The whip-like tail on many bacteria (known

---

[127] Michael J. Behe, *Darwin's Black Box: The Biochemical Challenge to Evolution* (New York: Free Press, 2006), 39.

[128] G. Cuvier, *A Discourse on the Revolutions of the Surface of the Globe and the Changes thereby Produced in the Animal Kingdom* (Philadelphia: Carey & Lea, 1831), 59.

[129] A. Cressy Morrison, *Seven Reasons Why A Scientist Believes in God*, The Divine Life Society, http://www.dlshq.org/messages/sciblgod.htm.

as a bacterial flagellum) is so proficiently designed to aid the movement of bacteria, that this system is practically impossible to be explained by naturalistic processes alone. Dave Miller briefly describes this marvel:

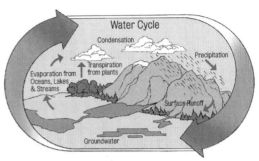

Figure 7.3 Water cycle.

> *The flagellar motor is similar to manmade motors—since both were built on fundamental principles set in place by the Creator. The flagellum consists of rotor and stator units in the cell membrane, including switching unit, bushing, universal joint, and helical screw propeller. To generate thrust, the rotary motor is driven by protons flowing into the cell body. The motor then drives the rotation of the flagellum at around 300 Hz, at a power level of 10-16 W, with energy conversion efficiency close to*

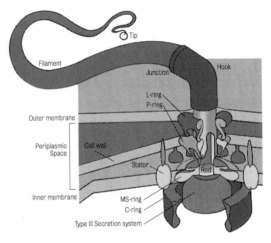

Figure 7.4 Bacterial flagellum.

> *100%. The resulting speed is up to 20,000 rpms—faster than the speed of Formula 1 race car engines. This highly efficient, flagellar motor is far beyond the capabilities of manmade, artificial motors. It is so sophisticated, that to suggest that it evolved is the height of irrationality and blind prejudice. Indeed, the evidence is decisive: there is a Designer.*[130]

Berkeley researchers have also specifically noted the systems involved in cellular propulsion in organic species to be illustrative of specified complexity and regularly study their astonishing motility processes.

---

[130] Dave Miller, "The Teleological Argument for the Existence of God [Part 1]." *Reason and Revelation* 38.2. http://apologeticspress.org/APPubPage.aspx?pub=1&issue=1264&section=0&article=2774&cat=329.

Fine-Tuning

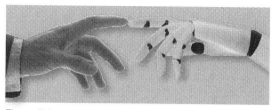

Figure 7.5

Fine-tuning is self-explanatory. In relation to ID, fine-tuning is the idea that everything in this universe is so precisely tailored to accomplish its purpose that naturalism alone cannot explain it. Among the common examples cited include the essential anthropic constants (e.g. distance from the sun, moon, Jupiter; gravity, atmosphere) that we will explore in greater detail in the next chapter.

To use a more tangible, everyday illustration, a fine-tuned car operates efficiently toward the goal of its tuner. A muscle car is designed for horsepower; a truck is designed for payload capacity and towing capability. Our universe is infinitely more complex and has infinitely more evidence of tailoring and tuning. In fact, the strength of this evidence is so compelling, that one famous apologist was able to use this approach to convert an ardent atheist into a theist! Apologist Gary Habermas once debated atheist Antony Flew and used an illustration Flew could not overcome. Habermas put a picture of a prosthetic hand up and asked Flew if the hand was designed. Flew of course said yes. Habermas pressed him as to why he knew that to be the case. Flew responded by describing various elements and capabilities of the prosthetic hand. Habermas then put a picture of an actual human hand up and again asked Flew if it was designed. Habermas then proceeded to explain how the human hand was infinitely more complex and tailored than the prosthetic hand. Flew was abjectly defeated. In response to this and other ideas from the debate, Flew later wrote: *"The only satisfactory explanation for the origin of such 'end-directed, self- replicating' life as we see on earth is an infinitely intelligent Mind."*[131]

A Classic Example of Scientifically Arguing For ID

Figure 7.6

Over two hundred years ago, William Paley wrote a landmark work on teleology, namely ID, in his book *Natural Theology or Evidences of the Existence and Attributes of the Deity*. Sir Isaac Newton and other leaders of the scientific revolution upheld that the physical laws he had uncovered revealed the mechanical perfection of the workings of the universe to be akin to a watchmaker, i.e. God.

Paley argued that one may be able to naturally explain

---

[131] Antony Flew, *There Is a God: How the World's Most Notorious Atheist Changed His Mind* (New York: Harpercollins, 2008), 132.

Figure 7.7

Figure 7.8

away what in actuality is the intentional placement of a fireplace hearth, but one cannot reasonably dismiss a watch as being without design. He explains why this is the case:

> [When] we come to inspect the watch, we perceive (what we could not discover in the stone) that its several parts are framed and put together for a purpose, e.g. that they are so formed and adjusted as to produce motion, and that motion so regulated as to point out the hour of the day; that, if the different parts had been differently shaped from what they are, of a different size from what they are, or placed after any other manner, or in any other order, than that in which they are placed, either no motion at all would have been carried on in the machine, or none which would have answered the use that is now served by it.

He proceeds to explain why our limited knowledge regarding the process by which the watch was made, what role each individual part may serve, why the watch may fail to work as the designer intended, etc. does not cause us to deny a watchmaker. Towards the end of Chapter 3 in his work, he introduces another element into the equation while simultaneously drawing out some logical conclusions about the vastly inferior view of atheism:

> The conclusion which the first examination of the watch, of its works, construction, and movement, suggested, was, that it must have had, for the cause and author of that construction, an artificer, who understood its mechanism, and designed its use. This conclusion is invincible. A second examination presents us with a new discovery. The watch is found, in the course of its movement, to produce another watch, similar to itself; and not only so, but we perceive in it a system or organisation, separately calculated for that purpose. What effect would this discovery have, or ought it to have, upon our former inference? What, as hath already been said, but to increase, beyond measure, our

admiration of the skill, which had been employed in the formation of such a machine? Or shall it, instead of this, all at once turn us round to an opposite conclusion, viz. that no art or skill whatever has been concerned in the business, although all other evidences of art and skill remain as they were, and this last and supreme piece of art be now added to the rest? Can this be maintained without absurdity? Yet this is atheism. This is atheism; for every indication of contrivance, every manifestation of design, which existed in the watch, exists in the works of nature; with the difference, on the side of nature, of being greater and more, and that in a degree which exceeds all computation. I mean that the contrivances of nature surpass the contrivances of art, in the complexity, subtlety, and curiosity, of the mechanism; and still more, if possible, do they go beyond them in number and variety: yet, in a multitude of cases, are not less evidently mechanical, not less evidently contrivances, not less evidently accommodated to their end, or suited to their office, than are the most perfect productions of human ingenuity.[132] [133]

While some have critiqued various elements of Paley's argument, some warranted and some unwarranted, his main premise remains steadfast. This with over two centuries of incredible scientific advancement!

Current Organizations And Scientists That Uphold This Argument

Paley made his argument two centuries ago, but do scientists still use the same argument today? Time would escape us to exhaustively list the proponents of this argument in the scientific community. There are numerous advocates of ID, despite that we are commonly told that "real" scientists can only believe in macroevolution. While we do not agree with everything that these organizations and individuals stand for, we merely use this brief listing to make a point; namely, that plenty of scientists believe in intelligent design.

A few organizations that support ID include: *The Discovery Institute, Center for Science And Culture, Centre for Intelligent Design, International Society for Complexity, Information, and Design (ISCID), Physicians and Surgeons for Scientific Integrity, Answers in Genesis, Apologetics Press, and Truth in Science.* Many of the citations in this book come from scientists and publications out of these institutions.

A few individuals who have specifically done an incredible job at explaining

---

[132] William Paley, *Natural Theology*, Heritage of Faith, 12th ed. Reprint, (Chilicothe, OH: DeWard Publishing Co., 2010).

[133] Compare this reproductive ability to Flew's quote above.

Figure 7.9 Michael Behe

Figure 7.10
Stephen C. Meyer

how ID has scientific merit are Michael Behe and Stephen C. Meyer.

Michael Behe is a world-renowned biochemist and professor of Biological Sciences at Lehigh University in Bethlehem, Pennsylvania. His magnum opus is *Darwin's Black Box* where he explores the concept of irreducible and specified complexity. He also demonstrates that the vast complexity of organisms is amplified by the immense assortment of different organisms in our biosphere. He has also written *Darwin Devolves: The New Science Behind DNA That Changes Evolution*.

Stephen C. Meyer holds a Ph.D. in Philosophy of Science from Cambridge University. He is a former geophysicist and college professor but is now known primarily for his work at the Discovery Institute. He has written several landmark works including: *Darwinism, Design, and Public Education; Explore Evolution; Signature in the Cell: DNA and the Evidence For Intelligent Design;* and *Darwin's Doubt: The Explosive Origin of Animal Life And the Case For Intelligent Design*. His specialty is namely in DNA and the complexity of things like bacterial flagellum and the mechanism of blood clotting as well as his work with the fossil record, namely the Cambrian Explosion. He also departs from many by spending a great deal of his time exposing philosophical biases in proponents of evolution. On his public Facebook page, Meyer's work in this area draws attention to one key incident worthy of headlines:

Prior to the publication of Signature in the Cell, the piece of writing for which Meyer was best known was an August 2004 review essay in the Smithsonian Institution-affiliated peer-reviewed biology journal Proceedings of the Biological Society of Washington. The article laid out the evidential case for intelligent design, that certain features of living organisms--such as the miniature machines and complex circuits within cells--are better explained by an unspecified designing intelligence than by an undirected natural process like random mutation and natural selection. Because the article was the first peerreview publication in a technical journal arguing for ID, the journal's editor, evolutionary biologist Richard Sternberg, was punished by his Smithsonian supervisors for allowing Meyer's pro-ID case into print. This led to an investigation of top Smithsonian personnel by the U.S. Office of Special Counsel, widely covered in the media, including the Wall Street Journal and Washington Post. The fed-

eral investigation concluded that Sternberg had been wrongly disciplined and intimidated. The case led to widespread public indignation at the pressures placed on Darwin-doubting scientists not only at the Smithsonian but at universities around the U.S. and elsewhere.[134]

Again, while we do not agree with all that these institutions and individuals teach, their passionate defense of ID illustrates that science has in no way ruled out theism. In fact, the majority of these scientists personally believe in and defend biblical theism, and they utilize the resources of science to make this defense!

ID Answers the "God of the Gaps" Objection

As one can readily see, reputable, intelligent individuals and institutions are using the methodology of ID to make an argument for a Creator. The reasoning is obvious for this following—ID is proper science. However, one other subtler benefit of this approach should be acknowledged and briefly explained.

A standard criticism of Christian apologists is the claim that their arguments are from ignorance; a logical fallacy typically, memorably, and not so affectionately entitled the "God of the Gaps" fallacy. Intelligent Design provides a viable response to this criticism, which may or may not be justified depending on the apologist's tactics. As we will explore in the next few chapters, ID argues from the undeniable premise that we do in fact scientifically know the source of design and information programming—the mind. This source of design and programming is undeniable based on universal independent scientific observation and study. Arguing by means of ID and proceeding from this foundation can jettison one past this blacklisting and move one forward with his defense. Stephen Meyer explains this aspect of the ID argument:

[ID] attributes the origin of information in living organisms to thought, to the rational activity of a mind, not a strictly material process or mechanism. That does not make it deficient as a materialistic or mechanistic explanation. It makes it an alternative to that kind of explanation. Advocates of intelligent design do not propose intelligent causes because they cannot think of a possible mechanistic explanation for the origin of form or information. They propose intelligent design because they think it provides a better, more causally adequate explanation for these realities. Given what we know from experience about the origin of information, materialistic explanations are the deficient ones.[135]

---

[134] https://www.facebook.com/pg/drstephencmeyer/about/?ref=page_internal

[135] Stephen C. Meyer, *Darwin's Doubt: The Explosive Origin of Animal Life And the Case For Intelligent Design* (New York: Harpercollins, 2014), 395.

Given that macroevolution fails to provide a sufficient and believable accounting for origins, the dinosaurs, the fossil record, and other related issues, the theory is found wanting. But the coup de grâce comes when information and design are considered and independent evidence all points to a Creator in this analysis atop that which more properly relates to historical science issues.

Concluding Thoughts

In light of the robust, reasonable points that ID has to offer, which will be explored in greater detail in the ensuing chapters, it is far more reasonable to believe there is a personal Creator of this world than to believe it merely began of its own accord and built itself without any direction into what we observe today. Reason is not what stands in the way of drawing this common-sense conclusion; it's a volition, a will hostile to God. For the one open-minded and reasonable enough, looking at the evidence elicits a humble adoration of the Creator and a desire to know Him (Ps 8; Rom 11:33). Humbly acknowledging that He is our Creator, we see that repudiation of the cause for our existence (i.e. rebellion) is not only futile but brings calamity. Kicking against the goads benefits nobody and is only detrimental to us. Scoffing at the Potter doesn't change the fact that we are clay molded in His hands!

Bill Jahns writes, *"Life is not some simple mechanism that can be explained by blind evolutionary chance. Complex organisms give clear evidence of intelligent design."*[136] Undeniably, the Builder of all things is God (Heb 3:4). Recognition of His design leads to the realization that there is an expectation of our Creator and that we are responsible to what He desires of us (Ps 19). It's a simple step. He has revealed Himself through general revelation in creation and in specific revelation in the Bible. The law of God further leads us to Jesus the Nazarene. *"The Word became flesh and dwelt among us"* to show us to light and the pathway back to our Creator (John 1:14). If we are to be rational people, we cannot begin our quest to discover our true purpose until we accept these truths.

I hope and pray that you do. If you do, then it is a simple step to allow your faith to mature by rendering obedience to the gospel call. God created you; He alone has the power to save you from your rebellion. He can reshape and reform you back into His image through His Son. [136]

---

[136] Bill Jahns, "Evidence for Intelligent Design," Life, Hope, & Truth, https://lifehopeandtruth.com/god/isthere- a-god/intelligent-design/evidence-for-intelligent-design.

Thought Questions:

1. Define Intelligent Design.

_____

_____

_____

_____

2. Is ID a biblical idea, a scientific idea, or both?

_____

_____

_____

_____

3. Give one example that even secularists would agree is an example of ID.

_____

_____

_____

_____

4. Who was William Paley and what impact did his work have on natural theology?

_____

_____

_____

_____

5. How does ID answer the "god of the gaps" challenge to a Christian's apologetic?

_____

_____

_____

_____

CHAPTER 8

Anthropic Constants

As scientists continue to study the universe, the mounting evidence has many scientists being convinced of ID. For example, Michael Licona confidently writes, *"It is safe to say that what we have been discovering within astrophysics since 1965 certainly points to an intelligent Designer as the external agent who fine-tuned the universe so that life might appear."*[137] If we were to use William Paley's watch illustration from our former chapter, our world is

Figure 8.1

infinitely more fine-tuned than a diamond encrusted Rolex. The Rolex is scrap in comparison!

Our universe and everything that we see has a Designer. It is unreasonable to conclude otherwise in light of the vast evidence leading us to this rational conclusion. And if we are to be true to the biblical definition of "faith" (Heb 11:1), we need to examine this evidence if we are to be faith-full. Looking at this evidence should convert the most calloused atheist. It should also further soften the heart of even the most devout Christian.

So, we transition now into one particular area in which ID is manifestly illustrated— anthropic constants. Anthropic constants are highly precise and interdependent environmental conditions that make life possible. The Bible highlights the importance of this aspect of God's intelligent design of the world in Isa 45:18-19:

> For thus says the Lord, who created the heavens (He is the God who formed the earth and made it, He established it and did not create it a waste place, but formed it to be inhabited), 'I am the Lord, and there is none else. I have not spoken in secret, In some dark land; I did not say to the offspring of Jacob, 'Seek Me in a waste place'; I, the Lord, speak righteousness, Declaring things that are upright.'"

---

[137] Gary R. Habermas and Michael R. Licona, *The Case for the Resurrection of Jesus* (Grand Rapids: Kregel Publications, 2004), 178.

Note that this text comes from a prophet who spoke in the mid-700s B.C. nearly 2,800 years ago!

One scientist who has done much work in the indexing and explanation of these constants is an astrophysicist named Hugh Ross. He has a website, www.reasons.org, where he catalogues over 120 constants that are necessary for life to exist (the number increases commensurate with scientific advancement). Similarly, mathematician A. Cressy Morrison has calculated that for the Earth to possess all of the catalogued anthropic constants, that would require a 1 in 10^{138} chance. Astrophysicists are agreed that there are only 10^{70} atoms in the entire universe; therefore, although *theoretically* possible, these chances are impossible *in practice*.

While time prohibits our elucidation of these constants, we would like to look at three large-scale systems exhibiting anthropic constants that demonstrate design.[138] As we enumerate this small fraction of the total (about 10%), we will compare them to statements made in the Scriptures regarding their formation and purpose by the hand of God.

Our Designed Solar System

Gen 1:14-19 reads,

Then God said, "Let there be lights in the expanse of the heavens to separate the day from the night, and let them be for signs and for seasons and for days and years; and let them be for lights in the expanse of the heavens to give light on the earth"; and it was so. God made the two great lights, the greater light to govern the

Figure 8.2

day, and the lesser light to govern the night; He made the stars also. God placed them in the expanse of the heavens to give light on the earth, and to govern the day and the night, and to separate the light from the darkness; and God saw that it was good. There was evening and there was morning, a fourth day.

This passage makes clear that God designed and created our solar system, as well as what extends well beyond our solar system, with a purpose (cf. Job 38:31-33). The celestial bodies were primarily created to regulate time, seasons, and direction. Deists suggest that God's work ends here; however, Christians know that God also

---

[138] These examples are most of those in: Norman L. Geisler and Frank Turek, *I Don't Have Enough Faith to Be an Atheist* (Wheaton, Ill: Crossway Books, 2007). Unless otherwise noted, all references for the rest of this chapter are from this source.

actively sustains the universe since Col 1:15-17 reads,

He is the image of the invisible God, the firstborn of all creation. For by Him all things were created, both in the heavens and on earth, visible and invisible, whether thrones or dominions or rulers or authorities—all things have been created through Him and for Him. He is before all things, and in Him all things hold together.

All things hold together in Him! Is that not what inspired the pioneers of science to explore how this happens in the first place? So how exactly does this all work in our solar system?

Figure 8.3

Observe the position of the celestial bodies. Each body rotates around its own axis (Uranus even does this sideways!) while simultaneously revolving around the sun. It should also be known that the sun is not static but is also itself moving.[139] All of this movement exists in an exquisitely choreographed motion that allows mutually interactive gravitational balances to be beautifully fine-tuned. If the centrifugal force of planetary movements did not precisely balance the gravitational forces, nothing could be held in orbit around the sun. There are no strings, no fences, for *"He stretches out the north over empty space and hangs the earth on nothing"* (Job 26:7).

The Sun and Earth, being 92.96 million miles apart, are also positioned exactly as they need to be. A fraction closer or farther and temperature variation would render human life impossible. Furthermore, according to research physicist Jeffrey A. Zweerink, if the gravitational force were different by 0.00000000000000000000000000000000000001% (That's thirty-seven zeros!), our sun would not exist; therefore, neither would we!

The moon and the Earth are much closer, but still 238,900 miles separate. Again, perfectly distanced. Bring them one thousand feet closer and the continents would be covered by thirty to fifty feet of water twice daily! If a fraction further from each other, wave stagnation would kill plankton and end all life by exponentially

[139] See "StarChild Question of the Month for February 2000," High Energy Astrophysics Science Archive Research Center (HEASARC), Astrophysics Science Division (ASD) at NASA/GSFC, https://starchild.gsfc.nasa.gov/docs/StarChild/questions/question18.html: *"[The] Sun—in fact, our whole solar system—orbits around the center of the Milky Way Galaxy. We are moving at an average velocity of 828,000 km/hr. But even at that high rate, it still takes us about 230 million years to make one complete orbit around the Milky Way!"*

decreasing available oxygen levels and also inhibiting the water cycle. Change the proximity of the moon and nocturnal species would also be threatened, as would be most internal clocks![140]

The distance between planets also plays an integral role in the possibility of life on our planet. For example, Jupiter serves as a cosmic vacuum cleaner for the Earth. Jupiter's gravitational pull is constantly pulling asteroids and comets out of our path. Without Jupiter being where it is, life on Earth would be in jeopardy.

A few other anthropic constants that deserve special mention are the speed of light (299,792,458 m/s) and the strong and weak nuclear forces. All laws of physics are related to the speed of light. A variation would alter all other constants and seemingly preclude the possibility of life. Interestingly, the Bible describes light as the starting point of creation (Gen 1:1-5)! In fact, God is frequently referred to as the true source of light (e.g. Jas 1:17; Rev 22:5; etc.). The nuclear forces are likewise vital to our existence. If the strong nuclear force were taken away, the universe would structurally break down into quarks (i.e. subatomic particles). We are composed of atoms, so if atoms break down, so do we. Frank Heile (PhD Physics Stanford University) describes how vital the weak nuclear force is: *"Without the weak force . . . electrons would be massless particles. Atoms would be impossible and this would be a completely different universe. The only thing I can tell you for sure about that universe is that we would not be here to talk about it!"*[141]

Our Designed Earth

We begin to narrow our scope from the heavens to the Earth. We realize along with the psalmist, *"The heavens are the heavens of the Lord, but the earth He has given to the sons of men"* (Ps 115:16). Let's now consider this gift to the sons of men.

The Earth possesses an average orbital speed of 67,000 miles per hour. It rotates at approximately one thousand miles per hour, thus giving us a twenty-four hour day. If the rotation speed were slower, temperature differences would be too drastic between night and day for life to exist. If faster, atmospheric wind velocities would be too strong for life. The Bible even describes the set-course for rotation from the perspective of one on Earth: *"Also, the sun rises and the sun sets; and hastening to its place it rises there again"* (Eccl 1:5). The psalmist gives more detail:

---

[140] For more information on the moon, as well as a helpful set of references, see: Jerry Bergman, "The Moon: Required for Life on Earth" Institute for Creation Research, http://www/icr.org/article/moon-required-forlife- on-earth.

[141] "If the Weak Nuclear Force did not exist, how different would the universe be?", Quora, https://www.quora.com/If-the-Weak-Nucear-Force-did-not-exist-how-different-would-the-universe-be.

Their line has gone out through all the earth, And their utterances to the end of the world. In them He has placed a tent for the sun, Which is as a bridegroom coming out of his chamber; It rejoices as a strong man to run his course. Its rising is from one end of the heavens, And its circuit to the other end of them; And there is nothing hidden from its heat. (Ps 19:4-6)

The Earth is also tilted on its axis at 23.5 degrees. If the Earth's axis were tilted at a lesser or a greater angle, temperatures would become prohibitively extreme. God clearly has a reason for creating the Earth the way He did. He is the Master Architect and knows precisely what is needed for our surviving and thriving (cf. Ps 104:5; Prov 8:29; Isa 40:21; et al).

Did you know that even the dirt is important? The thickness of the Earth's crust plays a vital role in our lives. If thicker, too much oxygen would be transferred to the crust; if thinner, volcanoes and tectonic shifts would make life impossible. Are you impressed yet? God has most assuredly shown us from the foundations of the Earth that He is the Artificer (Job 38:4; Ps 18:7; et al).

Figure 8.4

Let's consider one more truth regarding the Earth itself. Normally, seismic activity is cause for concern, but did you know that seismic activity even plays a vital role in the functioning of our planet? Surely, greater seismic activity would annihilate life on Earth. Yet, if we were to divest ourselves of seismic activity this would also lead to our peril. You see, seismic activity stirs up vital nutrients from the ocean floor that are carried to the continents. Tectonic uplift feeds life![142]

Our Designed Atmosphere

Let's now consider one of many illustrations with a narrower example—the Earth's atmosphere. Early in Creation, the Bible relates the establishment of a barrier between the waters of the heavens and the Earth. This clearly seems to refer to the atmosphere. Gen 1:6-8 reads,

---

[142] While we are not covering moral issues for biblical theism in the scope of this book, this point does provide a response to the charge that God is not benevolent since seismic activity exists. God is in control of seismic activity (cf. Num 16; Job 9:5-6; Ps 60:2; Nah 1:5; et al). However, sin has also corrupted the Earth (Rom 8:20-22), and death reigns until Christ swallows up death in victory (1 Cor 15:54-57).

Then God said, "Let be an expanse in the midst of the waters, and let it separate the waters from the waters." God made the expanse, and separated the waters which were below the expanse from the waters which were above the expanse; and it was so. God called the expanse heaven. And there was evening and there was morning, a second day.

The Bible affirms the atmosphere is a creation of God with a programmed purpose. When we study the atmosphere, we find several other functions that allow life to exist on Earth.

One key life-allowing aspect of the atmosphere is its designed level of transparency. If the atmosphere were more opaque, not enough solar radiation would reach the Earth and life would be impossible. If the atmosphere were more transparent, we would receive too much solar radiation and life would not be possible. The atmosphere is the perfect curtain of protection. The Psalmist observes,

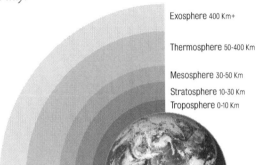

Exosphere 400 Km+

Thermosphere 50-400 Km

Mesosphere 30-50 Km

Stratosphere 10-30 Km

Troposphere 0-10 Km

Figure 8.5

Bless the LORD, O my soul! O LORD my God, You are very great; You are clothed with splendor and majesty, Covering Yourself with light as with a cloak, Stretching out heaven like a tent curtain," (Ps 104:1-2)

and Isaiah informs,

It is He who sits above the circle of the earth, And its inhabitants are like grasshoppers, Who stretches out the heavens like a curtain And spreads them out like a tent to dwell in" (Isa 40:22).

The atmosphere is also comprised of many layers containing many different elements and compounds (e.g. Nitrogen, Ozone, etc.) in a precise combination ensuring life is possible. Oxygen is at a perfect level (21%) to continue the breath of life from the mouth of God (Gen 2:7; Ps 150:6; Isa 42:5). If the levels were tweaked, this would prove catastrophic. If the level was 25%, there would be spontaneous combustion all over the earth and fires would cover the globe. If it were 15%, humans would suffocate. Carbon Dioxide is also at a perfect level. If the level were higher, a runaway greenhouse effect would develop, and mankind would literally roast to death. If the level were lower, plants could not maintain effective photosynthesis.

That means a breakdown in the plant kingdom that would cause total cataclysm in all other kingdoms. Additionally, plant death would also mean plankton and phytoplankton death, which would eliminate our Oxygen supply and render life impossible. The relationship between Carbon Dioxide and Oxygen is reciprocal. Humans exhale Carbon dioxide and plants use it to create Oxygen. Thus, we maintain the exact amount of Oxygen we need and the supply is constantly remanufactured.

Related to elemental composition is the fact of water vapor levels and their role in the atmosphere. Remember, Genesis teaches that God separated the waters (Gen 1:6-8; cf. also Job 36:29; 2 Pet 3:5). If the water vapor level were higher, a runaway greenhouse effect would cause temperatures to be unbearably hot. If lesser, insufficient greenhouse effect would cause temperatures to be unbearably frigid.

As with seismic activity within the Earth, there is also a force in the atmosphere that can be destructive, yet serves a vital purpose. Scientists refer to this is as the atmospheric discharge rate (ADR); non-professionals would simply identify this as the amount of lightning that strikes. The Bible affirms that God makes lightning (Ps 135:7; Jer 10:13; 51:16) and controls it (Job 28:26; 36:30, 32; 37:3-4, 11, 15; 38:35). If this rate were not tightly governed, catastrophe would result. If the ADR was greater, too much fire destruction would occur. If the ADR were lower, there would be too little Nitrogen transference into the soil.

Concluding Thoughts

Our world displays the handiwork of God, and it is our duty, privilege, and debt to glorify our Creator because of that observation. Reason dictates this responsibility. Cosmologist Ed Harrison states, *"Here is cosmological proof for the existence of God—the design argument of Paley—updated and refurbished. The fine-tuning of the universe provides prima facie evidence of deistic design."* British astrophysicist Fred Hoyle keenly points out that the arrangement that we see in nature forbids naturalistic causes. He contends,

I don't know how long it is going to be before astronomers generally recognize that the combinatorial arrangement of not even one among the many thousands of biopolymers on which life depends could have been arrived at by natural processes here on earth. Astronomers will have a little difficulty at understanding this because they will be assured by biologists that it is no so, the biologists having been assured in their turn by others that it is not so. The 'others' are a group of persons who believe, quite openly, in mathematical miracles. They advocate the belief that tucked away in nature, outside of normal physics, there is a law which performs miracles.[143]

[143] Fred Hoyle, "The Big Bang in Astronomy," *New Scientist* (Nov. 19, 1981): 526.

There is One to Whom we answer. He governs the universe, and as infinite and powerful as He is, He inhabited human form, and became dependent Himself on the anthropic constants He created to govern the universe. He became a baby in a manger and grew to become a man to redeem His people from the bondage of sin. He became meek to the point of death on our behalf—what a humbling thought!

I ask you to consider the evidence. And if that evidence leads you to the rational conclusion that there is a God of the universe, I hope you will choose to glorify your Creator. God inhabited human form to save you from your sins of betrayal against your purpose in Him. Let your faith lead you to answer His call for reconciliation!

I want to close this chapter with the text of Ps 65, which says,

There will be silence before You, and praise in Zion, O God, And to You the vow will be performed. O You who hear prayer, To You all men come. Iniquities prevail against me; As for our transgressions, You forgive them. How blessed is the one whom You choose and bring near to You To dwell in Your courts. We will be satisfied with the goodness of Your house, Your holy temple. By awesome deeds You answer us in righteousness, O God of our salvation, You who are the trust of all the ends of the earth and of the farthest sea; Who establishes the mountains by His strength, Being girded with might; Who stills the roaring of the seas, The roaring of their waves, And the tumult of the peoples. They who dwell in the ends of the earth stand in awe of Your signs; You make the dawn and the sunset shout for joy. You visit the earth and cause it to overflow; You greatly enrich it; The stream of God is full of water; You prepare their grain, for thus You prepare the earth. You water its furrows abundantly, You settle its ridges, You soften it with showers, You bless its growth. You have crowned the year with Your bounty, And Your paths drip with fatness. The pastures of the wilderness drip, And the hills gird themselves with rejoicing. The meadows are clothed with flocks And the valleys are covered with grain; They shout for joy, yes, they sing.

Thought Questions:

1. What are anthropic constants?

_____

_____

_____

_____

2. What does Isaiah record regarding God's formation of the Earth?

_____

_____

_____

_____

3. Pick one of the anthropic constants listed above and research it further. Record your observations.

_____

_____

_____

_____

4. Find an anthropic constant not detailed in this chapter and explain it.

_____

_____

_____

_____

5. Is it possible that an anthropic constant has ever been violated?

_____

_____

_____

_____

CHAPTER 9

The Designed Man

For You formed my inward parts; You wove me in my mother's womb. I will give thanks to You, for I am fearfully and wonderfully made; Wonderful are Your works, And my soul knows it very well. My frame was not hidden from You, When I was made in secret, And skillfully wrought in the depths of the earth; Your eyes have seen my unformed substance; And in Your book were all written The days that were ordained for me, When as yet there was not one of them. (Ps 139:13-16)

Shout joyfully to the LORD, all the earth. Serve the LORD with gladness; Come before Him with joyful singing. Know that the LORD Himself is God; It is He who made us, and not we ourselves; We are His people and the sheep of His pasture.

Enter His grates with thanksgiving And His courts with praise. Give thanks to Him, bless His name. For the Lord is good; His lovingkindness is everlasting And His faithfulness to all generations (Ps 100).

Appreciation For the Human Body

Rudolf Virchow, M.D., describes the human body as *"the most miraculous masterpiece of nature"* and calls it *"a pleasure to study . . . and . . . learn about the smallest vessel and the smallest fiber."*[144] Bestselling Mormon author Toni Sorenson agrees, concluding, *"Your body is a complete marvel. The more you study its anatomy and how each part works in harmony, the more you will be convinced that you didn't just evolve. You were designed from the beginning by the hand of a Master."*[145] One scientist powerfully writes and testifies to the reasonability of God's design of the human body and then explains how worldview clashes callous scientists to this rational conclusion. He argues,

Anyone who evaluates the evidence with an unbiased eye is forced to admit that the only logical conclusion is that the human body—just like the uni-

---

[144] Leslie Dunn, *Rudolf Virchow: Now You Know His Name* (Createspace, 2012), 8-9.

[145] Toni Sorenson, *The Great Brain Cleanse*, https://www.goodreads.com/work/quotes/49648693-the-greatbrain cleanse.

verse— demonstrates far too much complexity to have arisen by chance. It shows incredible design and purpose and many scientists recognize it. During my scientific training, I had the opportunity to spend one-on-one time with many brilliant minds. I talked to neurosurgeons, physicists, anatomists, molecular biologists, etc.—and in almost every case, they would admit that what we were studying was far too complex to have arisen by purely evolutionary processes. However, as soon as another individual walked into the laboratory, the scientist would drop the conversation and always toe the

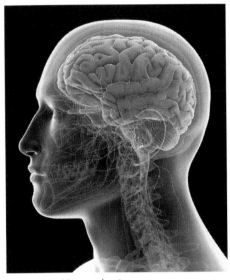

Figure 9.1 Human brain

evolutionary party line. After all, in many cases their positions were tethered to an allegiance of naturalism . . . . I have been asked on many different occasions if spending much time researching science has weakened my faith. On the contrary, it has strengthened my faith. My faith is firmly founded in evidence. I am convicted. The more layers I peel back the more I recognize the handiwork of God. Having reviewed material from every scientific field, I see a clear pattern. True science—science without the interpretations built on biases from ungodly men—points back toward the Creator. The scientific community is trained to collect data, report our findings, and then draw logical conclusions from our observations. The evidence for God is undeniable."[146]

There is no doubt by any thinking individual that the human body is immensely complex. Its purposeful complexity betrays its design from the outset (Gen 1:26-31). Consideration of just a few quick awe-inspiring details about the human body makes this conclusion rationally inescapable.

- The average person is made of seven octillion atoms! (7,000,000,000,000,000,000,000,000,000).
- People are made up of hundreds of trillions of cells! (RBCs, nerve cells, skin cells, etc.)
- There are a trillion nerves powering your memory!

---

[146] Brad Harrub, *Convicted: A Scientist Examines the Evidence For Christianity* (Brentwood, TN: Focus Press, 2009), 5175-5225 (Kindle Edition).

- If uncoiled, your DNA would stretch ten billion miles, from here to Pluto! If stretched out, the DNA contained in a <u>single</u> cell would be six feet long!

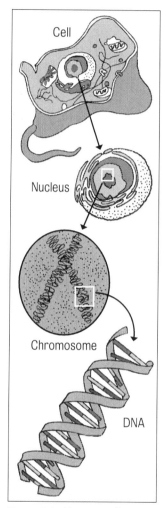

Cell

Nucleus

Chromosome

DNA

Figure 9.2 Human cell

As the psalmists above realized, we are fearfully and wonderfully made! The psalmists also acknowledged this truth elsewhere.

Many, O LORD my God, are the wonders which You have done, And Your thoughts toward us; There is none to compare with You. If I would declare and speak of them, They would be too numerous to count" (40:5);

"On the glorious splendor of Your majesty and on Your wonderful works, I will meditate" (145:5).

Who would reasonably conclude that this optimally designed and purposeful machine, unparalleled in complexity, could have been developed by successive, gradual, undirected changes a-la-macroevolution?[147] Darwin himself appreciated this complexity and included an entire chapter in his own *magnum opus* that describes organs of incredible complexity that posed challenges to his theory. He offered tentative solutions, but just as we saw with the fossil record, advances in science have destroyed his foundations. Darwin states, *"If it could be demonstrated that any complex organ existed which could not possibly have been formed by numerous, successive, slight modifications, my theory would absolutely break down."* Let's consider a few more examples of the human body in greater detail and refute Darwin's theory through both common sense and practical

---

[147] *"There is an elephant in the roomful of scientists who are trying to explain the development of life. The elephant is labeled 'intelligent design.' To a person who does not feel obliged to restrict his search to unintelligent causes, the straightforward conclusion is that many biochemical systems were designed. They were designed not by the laws of nature, not by chance and necessity; rather, they were planned. The designer knew what the systems would look like when they were completed, then took steps to bring the systems about. Life on earth at its most fundamental level, in its most critical components, is the product of intelligent activity."* Michael J. Behe, *Darwin's Black Box - The Biochemical Challenge to Evolution* (New York: Free Press, 2006), 193.

logic. We do this not merely to defend against an unacceptable view of our design, but also as a way to show our gratitude for the Lord. As the psalmist writes,

Praise the LORD! I will give thanks to the LORD with all my heart, In the company of the upright and in the assembly. Great are the works of the LORD; They are studied by all who delight in them. Splendid and majestic is His work, And His righteousness endures forever. He has made His wonders to be remembered; The LORD is gracious and compassionate (111:1-4).

Let's delight in the great works of the LORD as we study them!

Figure 9.3   Charles Darwin

Exquisite Detail in the Human Body

The Eye

The human eye is a wonder. It can distinguish between 2.3 and 7.5 million different colors. Plus, it has a resolution of 576 MP, while a top-of-the-line camera only offers about 40 MP. The eye also works at an incredible processing rate. J.K. Stevens summarizes the design of the eye with regards to this speed:

To simulate 10 milliseconds of the complete processing of even a single nerve cell from the retina would require the solution of about 500 simultaneous nonlinear differential equations one hundred times and would take at least several minutes of processing time on a Cray super computer. Keeping in mind that there are 10 million or more such cells interacting with each other in complex ways it would take a minimum of a hundred years of Cray time to simulate what takes place in your eye many times every second.[148]

In Darwin's chapter regarding organs of "exceeding perfection and complication," he admitted the rational problem the eye's complexity presented for his theory:

To suppose that the eye with all its inimitable contrivances for adjusting the focus to different distances, for admitting different amounts of light, and for

---

[148] John K. Stevens, *"Reverse Engineering the Brain,"* Byte, April 1985, 287.

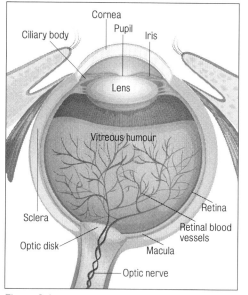

Figure 9.4

the correction of spherical and chromatic aberration, could have been formed by natural selection, seems, I freely confess, absurd in the highest possible degree [emphasis mine].

Evolutionist Sir S. Duke Elder agreed after further study:

Indeed, appearing as it does fully formed in the most primitive species extant today, and in the absence of transition forms with which it can be associated unless by speculative hypothesis with little factual foundation, there seems little likelihood of finding a satisfying and pragmatic solution to the puzzle presented by its evolutionary development.[149]

The Bible unequivocally teaches that God created the eye to serve man in his role to function as caretaker of the Earth. Prov 20:12 reads, *"The hearing ear and the seeing eye, The LORD has made both of them."* Ps 94:9 reads, *"He who planted the ear, does He not hear? He who formed the eye, does He not see?"* The Apostle Paul even uses the created role of the eye as basis for an analogy to members in the church in 1 Cor 12:16-17.

The Ear

The human ear is likewise a work of incredible design. Not only does it function so we can hear, but also so we can balance! It is interesting that God chose to create by audible speech (cf. Gen 1; Ps 33:6-9). He first spoke. Speaking requires sound and in order to be effective, requires a listener who hears. God has also used the medium of hearing in all ages to convey His will (e.g. Rom 10:17). Much akin to the eye, we see that God formed the ear (cf. Prove 20:12; Ps 94:9; 1 Cor 12:16-17). Let's observe a handful of elements of this optimal design.

Anatomically and physiologically, the ear is ideally suited. Sound is successfully transferred between three different mediums—from air in the outer ear, to

---

[149] William Stewart Duke-Elder, *The Eye in Evolution* (London: Kimpton, 1958), 247.

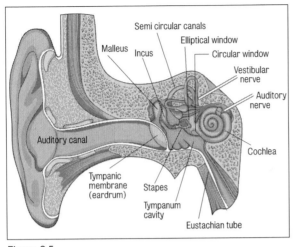

Figure 9.5

bone in the middle ear, to fluid in the inner ear. The three bones of the inner ear (hammer, anvil, stirrup) magnify sound waves by 120 dB and match impedance between air and water, preventing mitigation of the sound as it moves from air to fluid in the inner ear. As the sound waves move into the inner ear, various processes maintain pressure where it needs to be maintained and open channels to convey the signal. Eventually, cellular cilia and a molecular spring open a channel up to twenty thousand times per second that releases ions that change electrical charges, which then convey a neurological signal that is then interpreted by our brains as a sound! The shape and size of the auditory canal is particularly ideal for hearing the human voice, the wax and hair ideal for keeping foreign objects out, the laterally growing epidermal layer is ideal for clearing out excess wax.[150]

Even the sensitivity of the ear is incredible. The ear is sensitive to a change in air pressure of 1×10^{-10} atmospheres (i.e. the pressure occurring naturally at sea level). If we were to convey this in terms of altitude to make sense of the figure, it would be equivalent to a change in altitude of 1/30,000th of an inch ($^1/_{120}$th the size of a piece of paper). At four kHz, the eardrum responds to movements of $^1/_{10}$ diameter of a Hydrogen atom all while filtering out the reverberation of its own living tissue with parts much larger and making much louder noise![151]

The Appendages

Much could be said regarding human appendages (i.e. arms/hands/fingers and legs/feet/toes). Let's look at just a few elements that show immense complexity and purposeful design. Fingers can feel a ridge as small as thirteen nanometers in size ($^1/_{7500}$th the diameter of a human hair). Without the pinky finger, 50% of hand strength is lost. In terms of compression strength, the average adult male's femur

---

[150] For a fuller treatment of the eye and the ear, see the Answers in Genesis DVD, The Hearing Ear and the Seeing Eye where Dr. David Menton describes both in great detail.

[151] See previous footnote.

bone can withstand the weight of sixteen thousand people standing on it at once. Clearly, God has created man with incredible function to exercise dominion in this world (Gen 1) and in doing so He designed different elements to function in different, yet mutually beneficial functions (cf. 1 Cor 12).[152]

The Blood

The heart beats one hundred thousand times per day, pumping 5.5 liters per minute, and 3 million liters per year. This is done using the incredibly complex inner lining of the red blood cell plasma membrane. The efficiency and effectiveness of this process is mindboggling. Scientists such as Michael Behe and Stephen C. Meyer have also noted that the blood-clotting cascade is itself irreducibly complex. The process is comprised of twenty-three separate and necessary steps in succession. Without all of them happening in order, clothing doesn't occur. As if this were not enough, some stages interact with previous stages from steps much before the immediately previous stage. Make changes and the system fails; stop the process at any given step before the process is finished and blood-clotting does not occur.

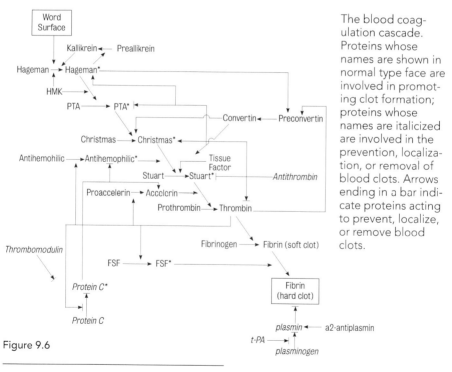

The blood coagulation cascade. Proteins whose names are shown in normal type face are involved in promoting clot formation; proteins whose names are italicized are involved in the prevention, localization, or removal of blood clots. Arrows ending in a bar indicate proteins acting to prevent, localize, or remove blood clots.

Figure 9.6

---

[152] Kate Ng, "18 Facts You Didn't Know About How Amazing Your Body Is," Independent, https://www.independent.co.uk/life-style/health-and-families/features/18-facts-you-didnt-know-abouthow- amazing-your-body-is-a6725486.html.

This is illustrative of irreducible complexity! Michael Behe makes this conclusion: *"Blood coagulation is a paradigm of the staggering complexity that underlies even apparently simple bodily processes. Faced with such complexity beneath even the simple phenomena, Darwinian theory falls silent."*[153] Hemoglobin, the intricate protein that transports oxygen in RBCs, is likewise a powerful illustration of God's design of the blood.[154] The Scriptures clearly state that the "life is in the blood" (Lev 17:11; Deut 12:23). Since God is the Creator of life, He is also the Giver of blood, a most precious commodity. And blood is clearly designed, thus necessitating a Designer.

The Cell

Recall Darwin's quote earlier where he stated that if irreducible complexity could be shown that his theory would crumble. We have seen several illustrations of this, but creation scientists particularly draw attention to the human cell. Michael Behe calls it "Darwin's black box." He did this because in Darwin's time, the cell was hypothesized to be quite simple, but scientists have shown this to be completely false. A single cell exhibits irreducible complexity and the human body contains hundreds of trillions of cells! Each of these individually demonstrates functional irreducible complexity as well (e.g. movement via cellular cilia and protein transport). Cells also play an integral role in the immune system. Their role is also irreducibly complex because the cascade has individual steps that are contingent on previous steps, yet that are also independent in development, just like blood

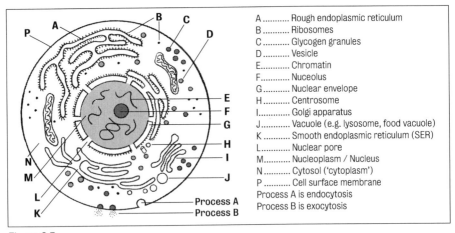

A .... Rough endoplasmic reticulum
B .... Ribosomes
C .... Glycogen granules
D .... Vesicle
E .... Chromatin
F .... Nucleolus
G .... Nuclear envelope
H .... Centrosome
I .... Golgi apparatus
J .... Vacuole (e.g. lysosome, food vacuole)
K .... Smooth endoplasmic reticulum (SER)
L .... Nuclear pore
M .... Nucleoplasm / Nucleus
N .... Cytosol ('cytoplasm')
P .... Cell surface membrane
Process A is endocytosis
Process B is exocytosis

Figure 9.7

---

[153] Behe, *Darwin's Black Box*, 97.

[154] For an excellent discussion on the merits of hemoglobin in the ID discussion and why macroevolution fails to explain this marvelous protein, see: Frank Sherwin, "Phenomenally Designed Hemoglobin," Institute for Creation Research, http://www.icr.org/article/phenomenally-designed-hemoglobin.

clotting. Three precise areas of the cellular role of the immune system which show irreducible complexity include clonal selection, antibody diversity, and complement system. On top of all this, cellular repopulation occurs in the body at a rate commensurate with the wear and tear of that particular area. This includes a complete changeover of five days for the stomach and intestines, two to four weeks for the skin, less than six months for RBCs, a couple of years for the liver, and about ten years for skeletal cells. Much of our body is refreshed every seven to fifteen years![155]

So what does the Bible say regarding the creation of the cell? Well, not a whole lot specifically since this terminology is of recent genesis. However, at least two key passages would include God's creation and programming of cells: *"All things came into being through Him, and apart from Him nothing came into being that has come into being"* (John 1:3); *"For by Him all things were created, both in heavens and on earth, visible and invisible, whether thrones or dominions or rulers or authorities— all things have been created through Him and for Him"* (Col 1:16).

Bacteria

Bacteria normally get an exclusively bad-rap; however, it is essential to our livelihood, especially our digestive process. The human gut (i.e. microbiome) actually has the highest known cell density of any microbial habitat on Earth! Did you also know that several pounds of your body are made up of bacteria? Pretty gross right? Even grosser is the fact that a single tooth in your mouth has between one hundred million and one billion bacterium! Makes you want to go brush your teeth! Bacteria also help us think and aid our central nervous system, and they aid our immune system by means of a "microbiome-gutbrain axis" in which amazing speed of communication takes place! Our natural bodily bacteria serves useful and necessary purposes! They also show irreducible complexity in many cases. The motility of bacteria via bacterial flagellum is a perfect illustration. While bacteria does not get treatment in the Scriptures, Christians do often sing the hymn "Our God, He Is Alive," which was written by A.W. Dicus. One line in the song says, *"God holds the germ within His hand."* Certainly, all creatures great and small are at His command, including the germ (i.e. bacteria).[156]

---

[155] Meghan Bartels and Florence Fu, "Most of the cells in your body die many times in your life — here's how often they regenerate," Business Insider, https://www.businessinsider.com/how-old-are-cells-cellularlifespan- 2016-8.

[156] For more information on the vital processes that bacteria are involved in within the human body, ICR has two brief, helpful articles. See: Frank Sherwin, "How Bacteria Help Our Bodies Survive," http://www.icr.org/article/bacteria-help-us-survive. See also: Brian Thomas, "Bacteria Make Good Linguists and Electricians," http://www.icr.org/article/bacteria-make-good-linguists-and-electricians.

What about "Poor Design," "Vestigial Organs," And "Junk DNA"?

Examination of the human body necessarily implies a designer—that Designer is God! However, many naturalistic scientists have responded to these marvels with skepticism and have argued that if God does exist, He is a terrible Designer. In this line of thought, Richard Dawkins infamously calls God "the Blind Watchmaker." Critiques abound but are easily refuted upon cross-examination. Two classic illustrations of "poor design" include

Figure 9.8

the retina being upside down and the existence of a hole in the back of the eye for the optic nerve. Atheistic scientists ridicule the notion of God because they believe these and other examples illustrate poor design. But is that the case? No, most certainly not. Scientists have repeatedly shown the functional advantages of these two examples in particular!

Another commonly cited proof that God cannot exist because of poor design is the human genome. Dr. Francis Collins and the Human Genome Project decoded the human genome in 2003. They found that only 1.5% of DNA was used to code proteins. They dismissed the other 98.5% as purposeless "junk DNA" left over from supposed evolution. They considered this a slam-dunk against Bible believers. However, they overlooked the fact that this other DNA held non-protein-producing functions such as regulating transcription, controlling RNA processing, editing and splicing, regulating embryonic development, and thousands of other functions. Consequently, there is no "junk DNA."

In 2012, the ENCODE project (short for Encyclopedia of DNA Elements) revealed these and other significant biological functions in at least 80% of the genome. There is little doubt that further studies will explain the remaining percentage as we develop our knowledge of DNA physiology. Amazingly, shortly after the release of ENCODE's findings, the renowned theoretical evolutionist Dan Graur (who has clearly been clamorously antagonistic toward the ENCODE project) admitted: *"If ENCODE is right, then evolution is wrong."*[157] Another team of genome researchers tested diverse data from across the globe in a statistical model for neu-

---

[157] D. Klinghoffer, "Dan Graur, Darwin's Reactionary," *Evolution News & Science Today*, https://evolutionnews.org/2017/06/dan-graur-darwins-reactionary.

tral evolution and found that 95% of the human genome could not possibly have evolved randomly![158]

Job also wondered at God's order and at times showed difficulty in accepting the way God designed and ran the world. God responded to his lack of understanding and challenges in Job 38-41. In response to God, Job states halfway through,

> Behold, I am insignificant; what can I reply to You I lay my hand on my mouth. Once I have spoken, and I will not answer; Even twice, and I will add nothing" (Job 40:4-5).

After God completes His rebuke, Job adds,

> I know that you can do all things, And that no purpose of Yours can be thwarted. "Who is this that hides counsel without knowledge?" Therefore I have declared that which I did not understand, Things too wonderful for me, which I did not know. "Hear, now, and I will speak; I will ask you, and you instruct Me." I have heard of You by the hearing of the ear; But now my eye sees You; Therefore I retract, And I repent in dust and ashes. (Job 42:2-6)

While God does not present Himself as directly as He did to Job, these things were written for man's instruction. Our knowledge is totally inadequate when measured against God's (Isa 55:8-9). Let's examine several key areas where this criticism fails to measure up.

First, the argument demands perfection. One has to be able to conceive of perfection for this to be possible. This quickly devolves into a demonstration of the ontological argument for God, and, certainly, atheists do not want to do that! Also, it overlooks the observed fact that designers do not always make the best designs. Most commodities we see today have a built-in obsolescence. Biblically, this is true for our bodies (cf. 2 Cor 5:1-5). Moreover, perhaps the Designer has multiple motives, with perfect design taking a backseat to other roles such as aesthetics or as a blockade for fleshly pride (cf. Job 38:2-3; 40:2; 1 Cor 12:18).

Second, the argument depends on psychoanalysis of the Designer. The reasons the Designer has done something cannot be determined without appealing to their stated reasons for doing something. The critic has to borrow from the Bible while simultaneously denying the Bible is reliable (Job 40:7-9)! The design of a feature may have an as-yetundetermined purpose or it could simply be for variety. Tonsils were once considered vestigial until an immune role was discovered. The same is

---

[158] F. Pouyet et al. 2018. Background selection and biased gene conversion affect more than 95% of the human genome and bias demographic inferences. *eLife*. DOI:10.7554/eLife.36317.

true of the appendix, gallbladder, and other organs in our bodies.[159] Further, imperfections often illustrate design better than perfection. A skin tear heals faster than a surgical cut of the same size.[160] God can be glorified in imperfection, and, sometimes, He allows imperfections that seem unjustified (John 9). As Behe remarkes, "*When it is considered by itself—away from logically unrelated ideas—the theory of intelligent design is seen to be quite robust, easily answering the argument from imperfection.*"[161]

Thirdly, and related, the negative psychoanalysis of the Designer is used as positive support for undirected evolution, a true argument from ignorance! In regards to the "imperfection of the eye," Michael Behe highlights this issue:

> *The scientific literature contains no evidence that natural selection working on mutation can produce either an eye with a blind spot, an eye without a blindspot, an eyelid, a lens, a retina, rhodopsin, or retinal. The debater has reached his conclusion in favor of Darwinism based solely on an emotional feeling of the way things ought to be.*[162]

Fourthly, the argument overlooks that the Bible explains such aberrations with a plausible and sound explanation—sin. Sin is so powerful it corrupts even DNA and environmental conditions (cf. Rom 8). God is still good! We asked a Christian how she viewed the benevolence of God in light of this difficulty. Her experience has been both personal and professional. She lost her teenage son to complications resulting from the mistreatment of his immunodeficiency. She also currently works with a company that facilitates treatment for those with immunodeficiency. I asked her, "What type of mentality does she, as a Christian, maintain when faced with the failures of the immune system?" Her answer was simple and straightforward:

---

[159] Charles Darwin was perhaps the first person to claim vestigial organs as an evidence for evolution. In chapter 13 of his Origin of Species, Darwin discusses what he calls "rudimentary, atrophied and aborted organs" that bore "the plain stamp of inutility" and were "extremely common or even general throughout nature." He speculates that they were merely leftover from precursor forms. He even lists about a dozen in his book The Descent of Man, including the muscles of the ear, wisdom teeth, the appendix, the coccyx, and body hair. The list grew in 1893 when German anatomist Robert Wiedersheim expanded the list to 86 vestigial organs. Scientists have resolutely shown that there are no such vestigial organs and the lists have been rendered obsolete. For an excellent article on this subject, see: David Mention, "Vestigial Organs—Evidence for Evolution?", The New Answers Book 3. Online: https://answersingenesis.org/human-body/vestigialorgans/ vestigial-organs-evidence-for-evolution.

[160] Healing times and effectiveness between vaginal and caesarean births illustrate this exquisitely.

[161] Behe, Darwin's Black Box, 228.

[162] Behe, Darwin's Black Box, 224

I always default to it being a part of God's plan that I don't understand completely now but I will understand one day. God created perfection. Decay began when sin came into the world, but I don't think that in any way reflects negatively on the designer, just as a bad battery or external factor may cause a clearly designed watch to stop working.

To question God's design is dangerous and ignorant. We are warned of this truth repeatedly in the Scriptures.

You turn things around! Shall the potter be considered as equal with the clay, That what is made would say to its maker, "He did not make me"; Or what is formed say to him who formed it, "He has no understanding"? (Isa 29:16).

Woe to the one who quarrels with his Maker— An earthenware vessel among the vessels of the earth! Will the clay say to the potter, "What are you doing?" Or the thing you are making say, "He has no hands"? Woe to him who says to a father, "What are you begetting?" Or to a woman, "To what are you giving birth?" (Isa 45:9-10).

On the contrary, who are you, O man, who answers back to God? The thing molded will not say to the molder, "Why did you make me like this," will it? Or does not the potter have a right over the clay, to make from the same lump one vessel for honorable use and another for common use? (Rom 9:20-21).

Concluding Thoughts Regarding the Intelligent Design of Mankind

"My soul knows it very well." There is a God! He has revealed Himself in exquisite detail, especially in the human form. He is *the God that we should know, Who speaks through His inspired Word!* To deny God in light of this available and copious evidence is foolishness (Ps 92:5-6). Science has not disproven God, least of all by studying those created in His image.

The evidence tells us that there is a Designer of each of us. As with all designed things, we have a purpose that is given to us by our Designer. He could have created us any way, for any purpose. He created us as we are—free thinking moral agents whose bodies, although exquisitely designed, will inevitably break down (cf. 2 Cor 4-5). What truly gives us meaning is that our bodies are inhabited by a spirit, which will continue after our bodies decompose. Our spirit, given by God, will either go back to God or be banished from God for all eternity. This reality expresses itself in

Heaven and Hell, for, *"Without heaven and hell, this incredibly designed universe is a stairway to nowhere."*[163] We hope that you will choose Heaven by pursuing God's desire for you—submission to His Son and repentance from your sins.

---

[163] Norman L. Geisler and Frank Turek, *I Don't Have Enough Faith to Be an Atheist* (Wheaton, Ill: Crossway Books, 2007), 387.

Thought Questions:

1. What does Psalm 139 say of mankind? What scientific concepts tie to this?

_____

_____

_____

_____

2. What example of design in the human body most amazes you?

_____

_____

_____

_____

3. Which is more advanced, the human eye or the world's most advanced camera?

_____

_____

_____

_____

4. When challenged with examples of poor design, how can Christians successfully respond?

_____

_____

_____

_____

5. What is ENCODE? What has it done to advance the apologetic of creationists?

_____

_____

_____

_____

CHAPTER 10

Information

Our previous chapter briefly examined several bodily systems that demonstrate ID. The discussion in this chapter is an expansion of the previous, but will also consider in more detail the concept of information programming in those and other systems. Much deserved appreciation is due to the information from scientists and theorists who have advanced the apologetic of God in these highly technical areas!

The Importance of Information And Programming

Let's consider an analogy. In any given backyard, there are to be found an assortment of stones of different sizes, shapes, types, and placement. The likelihood of this exact assortment of variables is astronomical, yet the arrangement is undeniable when looking at it. Let's consider now that we examine the same backyard and find the following phrase spelled out with rocks: *"Eric Parker is the best preacher and writer in the world!"* The likelihood of this placement is incredibly unlikely as well, but the main difference here is the conveyance of information. There is a message that is undeniably written in this set of stones. Who would reasonably deny that someone wrote this message using the stones? Imagine now that the stones themselves are all the same exact shape and type, with exactly one inch between each stone, a foot between each letter, and six feet between each word. What would the rational conclusion be?[164]

We share this story because naturalists are sometimes unjustifiably critical of Christians' biased interpretations of evidence. The challenge is often issued to ID that one cannot objectively determine design without accepting design a priori. This is a deception. However, one can reasonably deduce and detect design because it is evident when you have a number of separate components interacting in such a way as to intelligently accomplish a function beyond the scope of those individual components. As the specificity increases, so does the confidence of the deduction. What we see in nature clearly has manifold complexity and information conveyance; therefore, the deduction of intelligent design is one to be accepted with incredible confidence. In other words, what we observe and what scientists observe is programmed information whose programming has origin in the God of the Bible.

---

[164] This illustration has been adapted from Todd Chandler, professor of science at Florida College. The author heard him use it in a series of evidences lessons entitled "When Faith Meets Science" in 2016 at the Eastland church of Christ in Louisville, Kentucky.

Further Trademarks of Information

Dr. Werner Gitt has an excellent work in which he explores the essential characteristics of information and programming. In Part 2 of his work, he explores different aspects of information and develops a series of thirty key observations about information. These thirty observations categorically dismiss the possibility of information originating in purely materialistic processes and provide a strong scientific apologetic for an intelligent Designer, namely the biblical God. He summarizes the importance of these by highlighting seven key points of argumentation:[165]

1) There can be no information without a code.[166]
2) Any code is the result of a free and deliberate convention.
3) There can be no information without a sender.
4) Any given chain of information points to a mental source.
5) There can be no information without volition (will).
6) There can be no information unless all five hierarchical levels are involved: statistics, syntax, semantics, pragmatics, and apobetics.[167]
7) Information cannot originate in statistical processes.

To this he adds his later observation that information storage systems are also a telltale giveaway of intelligent design. We encourage the reader to reference his work for more material in regards to the details establishing the validity and logic of these observations as well as information theory. These observations are, however, undeniable and unavoidable in light of ubiquitous scientific research and inquiry. As Gitt remarks in his work: *"All created systems originate through information.*

---

[165] Werner Gitt, *In the Beginning Was Information: A Scientist Explains the Incredible Design in Nature* (Green Forest, AR: Masters Books, 2007), 80.

[166] Of the nature of code Gitt says, *"A code is a necessary prerequisite for establishing and storing information. Every choice of code must be well thought out beforehand in the conceptual stage. Devising a code is a creative mental process. Matter can be a carrier of codes, but it cannot generate any codes"* (69).

[167] He explains the importance of these five areas as the five aspects of information: *"A complete characterization of the information concept requires all five aspects—statistics, syntax, semantics, pragmatics, and apobetics, which are essential for both the sender and the recipient. Information originates as a language; it is first formulated, and then transmitted and stored. An agreed-upon alphabet comprising individual symbols (code), is used to compose words. The then (meaningful) words are arranged in sentences according to the rules of the relevant grammar (syntax), to convey the intended meaning (semantics). It is obvious that the information concept also includes the expected/implemented action (pragmatics), and the intended/achieved purpose (apobetics)"* (60).

A creative source of information is always linked to the volitional intent of a person; this fact demonstrates the nonmaterial nature of information."[168]

Amazing And Complex Design Is Observed in Biological Systems

As we have seen already, from a macro-scale to a micro-scale, design is evinced in many observable systems. Our universe functions purposefully, not chaotically. Our solar system is pre-programmed in a way unparalleled in complexity. Our bodies are programmed with information with which computer systems cannot begin to compare. The amount of information-processing events occurring daily in the human body is 3 x 10^{24} bits, over a million times the total amount of human knowledge stored in libraries around the world (i.e. 10^{18} bits)! Everything we see is daily testifying as an exhibition of our Maker. He communicated information into those systems to function; He also communicates to us so that we may function as we ought (2 Tim 3:16-17). All natural laws about information fit completely into the biblical message of the creation and sustenance of life (cf. Gen 1; John 1; Col 1).

Biochemist professor Michael Behe summarizes the issue for the naturalist well:

It was once expected that the basis of life would be exceedingly simple. That expectation has been smashed. Vision, motion, and other biological functions have proven to be no less sophisticated than television cameras and automobiles. Science has made enormous progress in understanding how the chemistry of life works, but the elegance and complexity of biological systems at the molecular level have paralyzed science's attempt to explain their origins. There has been virtually no attempt to account for the origin of specific, complex biomolecular systems, much less any progress. Many scientists have gamely asserted that explanations are already in hand, or will be sooner or later, but no support for such assertions can be found in the professional science literature. More importantly, there are compelling reasons—based on the structure of the systems themselves—to think that a Darwinian explanation for the mechanisms of life will forever prove elusive.[169]

Let's briefly consider five universal examples from biology that illustrate information programming and information storage systems. Those five examples are the brain, DNA, cells, molecular machines, and cilium and flagellum.

---

[168] Gitt, In the Beginning, 53.

[169] Michael J. Behe, *Darwin's Black Box: The Biochemical Challenge to Evolution* (New York: Free Press, 2006), x.

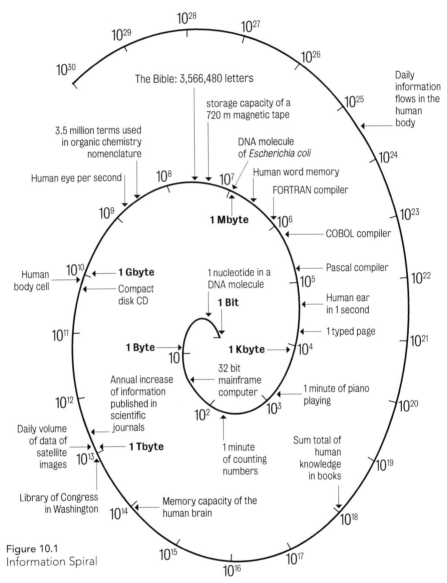

Figure 10.1
Information Spiral

The Brain

Perhaps the most fundamental element of ID, particularly in the realm of information and programming, concerns the necessary cause of a mind. What greater element to consider first as an illustration than the physical matter through which the human mind operates?

The human brain is one of the greatest examples of an information storage system in existence. Astronomer Carl Sagan admitted this truth four decades ago:

The information content of the human brain . . . would fill some twenty million volumes, as many as in the world's largest libraries. The equivalent of twenty million books is inside the heads of every one of us. The brain is a very big place in a very small space . . . The circuitry of a machine more wonderful than any devised by humans.[170]

To help us visualize that, twenty million volumes would be equivalent to if you stacked one thousand books on all twenty thousand seats in Madison Square Garden! This admission is powerfully illustrative of incredible complexity, yet this even seems to be an underestimate based on more recent studies![171] Consider too that the human brain is also served by an electrical system served by trillions of nerve cells!

DNA

Deoxyribonucleic acid (DNA) has been the source of infinite research with the lightyear improvements in microscopy and other various advances in technology. DNA is what makes any biological system function; it's what makes a person a person, a monkey a monkey, a beetle a beetle. The DNA molecule is very long and thin (nineteen million times longer than its width). The DNA in a single cell is approximately six feet long when stretched out, multiply this by an estimated fifty trillion cells in the body, and it would stretch to the sun and back six hundred times! DNA contains a six-billion-letter string of code that forms the human genome![172]

DNA is chemically comprised of a double-helix bond made up of a quaternary code of adenine, thymine, cytosine, and guanine. This genetic code is not accidental and arbitrary, but rather optimized from an engineering standpoint by several factors including a small and even number of symbols, ideal suiting for the ease of correcting errors, and intuitive design for the maximization of storage density. To illustrate this complexity on a different level, Chromosome 1 has 270 million base pairs whose representative letters would fill 200,000 pages! Still again, Dr. Gitt illustrates the complexity on yet another level:

---

[170] Carl Sagan, *Cosmos* (New York: Random House, 1980), 278.

[171] Dr. Werner Gitt, former Head of the IT Department at the German Federal Institute of Physics and Technology gives several estimates of various researchers of brain memory capacity in the amounts of between 1013 and 1015 bits, 3.9 x 106 bits (only concerning memorized words), 1.5 x 106 bits, and 2.65 x 1020 bits. Clearly, even quantifying such a high capacity is a difficult business! (*In the Beginning*, 190).

[172] Bo Kirkwood, *Creation Versus Evolution* (Athens, AL: Truth Publications, 2017), 35.

[The] amount of information is so immense in the case of human DNA that it would stretch from the North Pole to the equator if it was typed on paper, using standard letter sizes. The DNA is structured in such a way that it can be replicated every time a cell divides in two. Each of the two daughter cells must have identically the same genetic information after the division and copying processes. This replication is so precise, that it can be compared to 280 clerks copying the entire Bible sequentially each one from the previous one, with, at most, one single letter being transposed erroneously in the entire copying process . . . When a DNA string is replicated, the double strand is unwound, and at the same time a complementary strand is constructed on each separate one . . . One cell division lasts from 20 to 80 minutes, and during this time the entire molecular library, equivalent to one thousand books, is copied correctly.

Amino acid	Genetic code	Abbr
Alanine	GCA GCC GCG GCU	Ala
Arginine	AGA AGG CGA CGC CGG CGU	Arg
Asparagine	AAC AAU	Asn
Aspartic acid	GAC GAU	Asp
Cysteine	UGC UGU	Cys
Glutamine	CAA CAG	Gln
Glutamic acid	GAA GAG	Glu
Glycine	GGA GGC GGG GGU	Gly
Histidine	CAC CAU	His
Isoleucine	AUA AUC AUU	Ile
Leucine	CUA CUC CUG CUU UUA UUG	Leu
Lysine	AAA AAG	Lys
Methionine	AUG	Met
Phenylalanine	UUC UUU	Phe
Proline	CCA CCC CCG CCU	Pro
Serine	AGC AGU UCA UCC UCG UCU	Ser
Threnine	ACA ACC ACG ACU	Thr
Tryptophan	UGG	Try
Tyrosine	UAC UAU	Tyr
Valine	GUA GUC GUG GUU	Val
Stop sign	UAA UAG UGA	

Figure 10.2 Life Enabling Twenty Amino Acids

Many scientists have seen the intricacy of DNA and have concluded that this is a powerful testimony to design. Antony Flew, the late and former ardent atheist, had this to say regarding DNA research: *"What I think the DNA material has done is that it has shown, by the almost unbelievable complexity of the arrangements which are needed to produce (life), that intelligence must have been involved in getting these extraordinarily diverse elements to work together."* Mike Riddle points out several of these diverse elements including only twenty of three hundred types of amino acids being compatible with life, physiological restriction to only left-handed shaped amino acids, the order of irreducible complexity in amino acids, and the chances of a single protein being just a hundred amino acids is 1 in $1x10^{130}$.[173] Scientists have also pointed out the four-dimensional dynamic programming of the genome: 1) DNA, 2) Interactions on the DNA, 3) Programming allowing it to still work as it wraps into folds, and 4) The genome changes shape over time. Add to this that the production of proteins requires DNA and the production of DNA requires

[173] Mike Riddle in: *The New Answers 3*, DVD, directed by Ben Hilt (Hebron, KY: Answers in Genesis, 2010).

[174] Attempts to find justification and proof of macroevolution in Hox genes and developmental gene regulatory networks (dGRN's) have wholly failed.

proteins! In effect, you cannot count on macroevolution to develop such a system since the development of individual factors cannot lead to this system.[174] Everything needs to work together at the same time to function properly, and it does! A Creator, Designer, Programmer is requisite!

Cells

Scientists have found wondrous involvedness on the microscopic level. Order is observed in the tiniest of substances. Cells illustrate this exquisitely and have been the focus of discussion with scientists like Michael Behe, Stephen C. Meyer, Werner Gitt, and other noteworthy creation scientists. There is no greater example of higher statistical packing density of information than what is found with the cell. For in-depth examination of the cell, referencing Meyer's *Signature in the Cell* will prove especially helpful. For our purposes, however, two quotes from the shorter and easier-to-read *Darwin's Black Box* will serve to illustrate several basic points.

> *The simplicity that was once expected to be the foundation of life has proven to be a phantom; instead, systems of horrendous, irreducible complexity inhabit the cell. The resulting realization that life was designed by an intelligence is a shock to us in the twentieth century who have gotten used to thinking of life as the result of simple natural laws.*[175]

> *Biochemistry has demonstrated that any biological apparatus involving more than one cell (such as an organ or a tissue) is necessarily an intricate web of many different, identifiable systems of horrendous complexity. The "simplest" self-sufficient, replicating cell has the capacity to produce thousands of different proteins and other molecules, at different times and under variable conditions. Synthesis, degradation, energy generation, replication, maintenance of cell architecture, mobility, regulation, repair, communication—all of these functions take place in virtually every cell, and each function itself requires the interaction of numerous parts.*[176]

To these quotes we would like to add Werner Gitt's quantification of information in a single human cell at 1.2×10^{10}. Compare that to his evaluation of the internal memory of a mainframe computer at 1.678×10^{10}.[177] Each human cell has nearly the information capacity of a mainframe computer! Yet, who would deny the computer was designed? Then what of the cell?!

---

[175] Behe, *Darwin's Black Box*, 252.

[176] Behe, *Darwin's Black Box*, 46-47.

[177] Gitt, *In the Beginning*, 190, 188.

Molecular Machines

Michael Behe also does a fantastic job elucidating the fascinating machinery that allows function in biological systems at the molecular level. Several quotes illustrate this well.

The cumulative results [of scientific inquiry into the composition of living things] show with piercing clarity that life is based on machines—machines made of molecules! Molecular machines haul cargo from one place in the cell to another along "highways" made of other molecules, while still others act as cables, ropes, and pulleys to hold the cell in shape. Machines turn cellular switches on and off, sometimes killing the cell or causing it to grow. Solarpowered machines capture the energy of photons and store it in chemicals. Electrical machines allow current to flow through nerves. Manufacturing machines build other molecular machines, as well as themselves. Cells swim using machines, copy themselves with machinery, ingest food with machinery. In short, highly sophisticated molecular machines control every cellular process. Thus the details of life are finely calibrated, and the machinery of life enormously complex.[178]

Because gated transport requires a minimum of three separate components to function it is irreducibly complex. And for this reason the putative gradual, Darwinian evolution of gated transport in the cell faces massive problems. If proteins contained no signal for transport, they would not be recognized. If there were no receptor to recognize a signal or no channel to pass through, again transport would not take place. And if the channel were open for all proteins, then the enclosed compartment would not be any different from the rest of the cell.[179]

Antibodies are the "fingers" of the blind immune system—they allow it to distinguish a foreign invader from the body itself . . . To make sure that at least one kind of antibody is available for each attacker, we make billions to trillions of them. Usually for any particular attacker, it takes 100,000 [antibodies] to find one antibody that works [to defeat the attacker].[180]

---

[178] Behe, *Darwin's Black Box*, 4-5.

[179] Behe, Darwin's Black Box, 109.

[180] Behe, Darwin's Black Box, 120-121.

Behe also points out that there are ten billion different combinations for antibodies that can be multiplied even further by other tricks the cell can use![181]

Cilia And Flagella

The benefits of the brain, DNA, cells, and molecular machines to biological systems are patently obvious. However, and as we have pointed out in a previous chapter, scientists have also noted beneficial aspects of the cilia and flagella which propel microscopic organisms such as bacteria. These apparently simple structures contain staggering complexity with a plethora of precisely designed parts. With the highly probable likelihood that even more complexity will be discovered in such systems, the chances of macroevolutionary origin and development plummets. Darwinian theory cannot now explain cilium or flagellum, nor will the problem be overcome in the future; information programming through ID (i.e. God) can and does explain them now and is capable of explaining them however many details are studied and uncovered.

The Naturalist's Response

So how do naturalistic scientists explain these clear examples of information storage systems and information programming? Creativity knows no bounds, and hypotheses, however ridiculous and unrealistic they may be, are innumerable. Rather than critique each individually, let's succinctly consider and rebut perhaps the most famous of these critiques. In mockery of creationists, British biologist Richard Dawkins wrote *The Blind Watchmaker*. In this work, Dawkins ridicules creationism and attempts to refute teleological arguments for God and what he refers to as the "appearance of design." A key element of his purported proof is his development of a simulated computer program that he believes imitates random mutation and natural selection, two requisites for evolutionary theory. The system adapts a phrase from Shakespeare's *Hamlet*, namely, *"Me thinks it is like a weasel."* The success of the computer in generating the phrase is taken to disprove ID.

Others have made similar attempts to mimic natural selection and random mutation, but they all suffer from the same issue—they all presuppose design, not disprove it! The system was designed by a mind, the amount of letters in the combinatorial sequences was selected, a regulatory protocol was input that allowed the computer to compare what was selected with the target phrase, and every other necessary factor had already been chosen by a mind! How ridiculous to think that this designed system proves random mutation and natural selection![182] On the

---

[181] Behe, *Darwin's Black Box,* 129.

[182] Vasubot, the Japanese organ-playing robot, is another example of an amazing, but designed, machine that is programmed to accomplish a task.

contrary, it shows ID and the telltale evidence of information's origin in the mind! Sadly, bias causes many otherwise brilliant scientists to totally miss the mark in seeing biological information for what it truly is—a fingerprint of God! Dr. Gitt again points out,

> *Because of the philosophical bias, both information and life itself are regarded as purely material phenomena in the evolutionary view. The origin and nature of life is reduced to physical-chemical processes . . . All such ideas have in common that biological facts are interwoven with subjective representations which cannot be justified scientifically.*[183]

The Bible Explains Information Programming; Naturalism Does Not[184]

Biochemist Michael Behe candidly reveals,

> *Biochemistry has, in fact, revealed a molecular world that stoutly resists explanation by the same theory so long applied at the level of the whole organism. Neither of Darwin's starting points—the origin of life, and the origin of vision—has been accounted for by his theory. Darwin never imagined the exquisitely profound complexity that exists even at the most basic levels of life . . . In the face of the enormous complexity that modern biochemistry has uncovered in the cell, the scientific community is paralyzed. No one at Harvard University, no one at the National Institutes of Health, no member of the National Academy of Sciences, no Nobel prize-winner—no one at all can give a detailed account of how the cilium, or vision, or blood clotting, or any biochemical process might have developed in a Darwinian fashion. But here we are. Plants and animals are here. The complex systems are here. All these things got here somehow: if not in a Darwinian fashion, then how?*[185]

Macroevolutionary and other naturalistic hypotheses are wholly insufficient to explain what we see. These irreducibly complex information systems possess a structurefunction relationship that excludes naturalistic processes. From the start, these systems require all of the details and encoding that they currently possess.

---

[183] Gitt, *In the Beginning*, 82.

[184] Part 3 of Werner Gitt's book applies the concept of information and programming to the Bible. He systematically explains according to the natural laws of information how the Bible is clearly a revelation of the mind of God. I encourage the reader to especially reference this practical part of his book.

[185] Behe, *Darwin's Black Box*, 173, 187.

The key benefit of ID and information science is that they cut out the "God of the gaps" accusation in discussions of the subject matter of this chapter. Also, ID eliminates the accusation of special pleading. We possess universal and independent research that shows that minds produce information. Yet human minds, as developed and amazing as they are, are wholly incapable of producing such structures as we see in biological systems. Avian aerodynamics, for example, exposes Airbus, Boeing, and Lockheed Martin's best designs to be child's play (something we will discuss further in the next chapter)! We must therefore go to a level beyond humankind; the most logical next step is a powerful Creator. And when we open our minds to an explanation, we see that general revelation of this Creator leads us to special revelation of His mind, something the inspired Apostle Paul writes of:

> *For to us God revealed them through the Spirit; for the Spirit searches all things, even the depths of God. For who among men knows the thoughts of a man except the spirit of the man which is in him? Even so the thoughts of God no one knows except the Spirit of God. Now we have received, not the spirit of the world, but the Spirit who is from God, so that we may know the things freely given to us by God, which things we also speak, not in words taught by human wisdom, but in those taught by the Spirit, combining spiritual thoughts with spiritual words* (1 Cor 2:10-13).

The Bible is the perfect revelation of information—the mind of God in coded, understandable form. What a gift! Dr. Werner Gitt summarizes different aspects of this perfect source of information by making the following observations:

> *- The Bible contains the most important information conceivable. It is divine in essence, and indicates the way to our Father's house.*

> *- The relevance value of the information of the Bible for every person is r = 1, the highest possible value. It comprises the best advice for this life, and is the only compass that guides us to heaven.*

> *- The information of the Bible is always up-to-date (t = 1). Whereas most scientific publications become outdated after ten years, the Bible can never become outdated.*

> *- We can readily access the information of the Bible (a = 1). It can be obtained all over the world, and the contents are easy to understand.*

> *- The information of the Bible is comprehensive and complete (e = 1).*

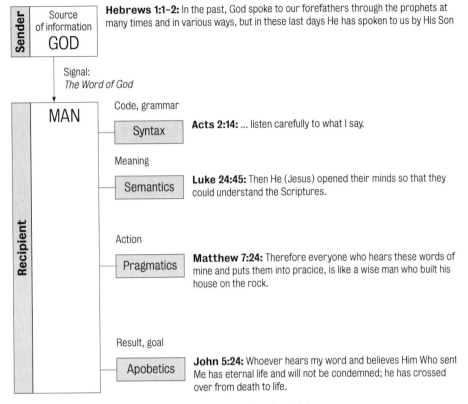

Figure 10.3 Perfect Communication Illustrated in The Bible

- *No false information is contained in the Bible; it is the only Book of truth (John 17:17).*

- *We find the highest semantic density of information in the Bible, as well as the best pragmatic information (commandments, rules of living, and our relationship with God and other people). It comprises the highest possible apobetics, namely an invitation to enter heaven!*[186]

Concluding Thoughts And Summarization

The existence of information, coding, and programming observed in biological systems clearly militates against naturalistic processes; they necessarily require a mind far advanced beyond our own. The God of the Bible undeniably provides the answer—God is Designer and Programmer! (Heb 3:4). He has left His

---

[186] Gitt, *In the Beginning*, 162.

code in us and in what we observe so that we are drawn to His information in the Bible, the greatest information product in the history of the world—the scheme of redemption and the love of God poured out in the death and resurrection of Jesus!

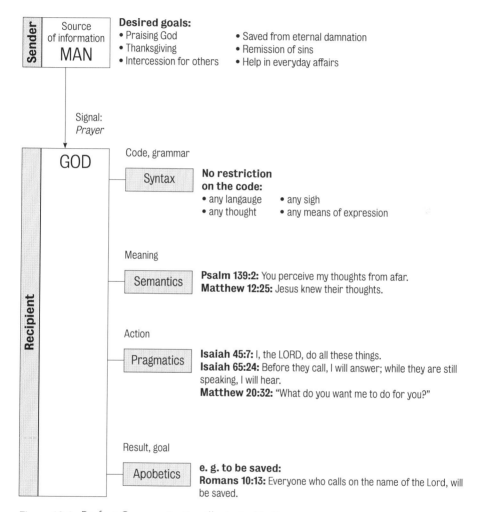

Sender

Source of information
MAN

Desired goals:
- Praising God
- Thanksgiving
- Intercession for others
- Saved from eternal damnation
- Remission of sins
- Help in everyday affairs

Signal: *Prayer*

GOD

Recipient

Code, grammar

Syntax

No restriction on the code:
- any langauge
- any thought
- any sigh
- any means of expression

Meaning

Semantics

Psalm 139:2: You perceive my thoughts from afar.
Matthew 12:25: Jesus knew their thoughts.

Action

Pragmatics

Isaiah 45:7: I, the LORD, do all these things.
Isaiah 65:24: Before they call, I will answer; while they are still speaking, I will hear.
Matthew 20:32: "What do you want me to do for you?"

Result, goal

Apobetics

e. g. to be saved:
Romans 10:13: Everyone who calls on the name of the Lord, will be saved.

Figure 10.4 Perfect Communication Illustrated in Prayer

Thought Questions:

1. How does a study of information and programming take ID to the next level?

_____

_____

_____

_____

2. What Bible passages establish principles important to this discussion?

_____

_____

_____

_____

3. How does the brain compare to a supercomputer?

_____

_____

_____

_____

4. What advantages does DNA gain by being programmed as a quaternary system?

_____

_____

_____

_____

5. What is the naturalist's response to this line of reasoning?

_____

_____

_____

_____

CHAPTER 11

Miscellaneous Biological Marvels

Before we close with our final chapter, we want to wrap up this series of latter chapters on design with one chapter on miscellaneous biological marvels found in the animal and plant kingdoms. Thus far the discussion has almost
exclusively focused on humans and for good reason, as mankind is the pinnacle
of creation (Gen 1:26-27).[187] Now, however, we direct our attention briefly to the
fields of botany and zoology.

The examples presented in this chapter are not all necessarily irreducibly complex, but they are nonetheless phenomenal examples of engineering. Each example
should cause one to wonder at the masterpieces of God's created order, even in
creatures not bearing His image.[188] As we look at these examples, do still keep in
mind the principles from preceding chapters, as they will help one appreciate the
signature of design present in each example. Keep in mind also that the imbalance
in presentation—more for animals and less for plants—is reflective of primary
scholarship in these fields as applied to Christian apologetics. Our hope is that this
imbalance will find more equilibrium and that more research, especially in Christian apologetics with regards to botany, will take place in the near future.

The Plant Kingdom

The Bible teaches that God created the plant kingdom on the third day of creation. Gen 1:9-13 reads,

---

[187]The exceptions to this have been alleged evolutionary predecessors and passing references to
the bacterial kingdoms.

[188] Contrast the evolutionary viewpoint, which contends that, *"Some life forms 'just happened'
to evolve the ability to reproduce asexually, while others 'just happened' to develop the capability
to reproduce sexually. Some life forms 'just happened' to evolve the ability to walk along vertical
ledges (e.g., geckos), while others 'just happened' to evolve the 'gift' of glowing (e.g., glow worms).
Some life forms 'just happened' to evolve the ability to make silk (e.g., spiders), which, pound-for-
pound, is stronger than steel, while others 'just happened' to evolve the ability to 'turn 90 degrees
in under 50 milliseconds' while flying in a straight line (e.g., the blowfly; Mueller, 2008, 213[4]:82).
Allegedly, everything has come into existence by random chances over billions of years. According to
the General Theory of Evolution, there was no Mind, no Intelligence, and no Designer that created
the Universe and everything in it."* Eric Lyons, "Wonders of God's Creation," *Reason and Revelation* 29.1, http://apologeticspress.org/APPubPage.aspx?pub=1&issue=609&section=0&ar-
ticle=722&cat=328). Despite believing this, evolutionists simultaneously admit and marvel at
what they admit is design in nature!

Then God said, "Let the waters below the heavens be gathered into one place, and let the dry land appear"; and it was so. God called the dry land earth, and the gathering of the waters He called seas; and God saw that it was good. Then God said, "Let the earth sprout vegetation, plants yielding seed, and fruit trees on the earth bearing fruit after their kind with seed in them"; and it was so. The earth brought forth vegetation, plants yielding seed after their kind, and trees bearing fruit with seed in them, after their kind; and God saw that it was good. There was evening and there was morning, a third day.

The Genesis account later specifies that plants were created specifically as a food source for mankind and for the other kingdoms (cf. Gen 1:29-30); however, this does not mean this is their only duty. As we have already seen in our chapter on anthropic constants, plants, particularly plankton and phytoplankton, play a pivotal role in Earth's oxygen saturation content. As with all creation, God created plants to serve key purposes in His creation and, as such, we would expect to see examples of design in this kingdom. In respect to the main purpose of this kingdom, these land plants would, from the beginning, require leaves, stems, flowers, seeds, roots, and fruits. The evolutionist denies this and claims all life, including plants, had an origin in the mysterious primordial soup. The evidence uniformly points to the Creator. Let's consider a few examples that are primarily taken from the research coming out of the Institute for Creation Research (ICR) as well as Apologetics Press.

Roots

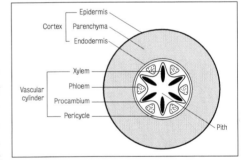

Figure 11.1 Root Cross-section

The root system, required immediately for land plants to serve their purpose at creation, has many components that are irreducibly complex. One illustration is the endodermis, which controls water and nutrient intake. The endodermis has a waterproof, corky band of tissue (i.e. the Casparian strip) around the transverse and radial walls of root cells that controls important physiological processes operating in irreducibly complex ways. All of this to ensure the plant survives by proper intake of nutrients, protection from disease, and maintenance of root pressure. Despite evolutionary hypotheses, the root system of plants defies materialistic explanation and gradual development.[189] God is at the root of this technological marvel.

---

[189] Frank Sherwin, "Secular Root Origins Appear Groundless," Institute for Creation Research, http://www.icr.org/article/secular-root-origins-appear-groundless.

Pine Trees

Dr. Dave Miller, Executive Director for Apologetics Press, has a helpful article on the witness of divine design in three specific species of pine trees: the Ponderosa Pine, the Lodgepole Pine, and the Whitebark Pine.[190] The Ponderosa Pine, for example, has a fascinating plate-like structured bark that is able to shed during forest fires. This segmentation, as well as the thickness, of the bark makes Ponderosa Pine trees resilient to fire. The Lodgepole Pine produces tiny pinecones that remain closed until the heat of a forest fire opens them. In effect, while the fire takes the life of the tree, the seeds of the tree are empowered by the fire to repopulate the forest! Miller also describes the symbiotic relationship between the Clark's nutcracker and the Whitebark Pine that allows food for the bird and reproduction of the tree. These three examples are powerful testimony to design, so powerful, in fact, that Miller opens the article with this striking statement:

Figure 11.2   Ponderosa Pine

Figure 11.3   Lodgepole Pine

> *The naturalistic explanation given by evolutionists for the existence of the created order cannot meet the dictates of logic that characterize the unencumbered, unprejudiced human mind. The more one investigates the intricacies and complexities of the natural realm, the more self-evident it is that a grand and great Designer is responsible for the existence of the Universe. In fact, the evidence is overwhelming and decisive.*

Figure 11.4   Whitebark Pine

After considering his three pine tree examples, he closes with another strong statement:

> *The interdependent, interconnected, interpenetrating features of God's Creation are beyond the capability of man to trace out—let alone to "manage" or "assist."*

---

[190] Dave Miller, "Divine Design and the Pine Tree," *Reason and Revelation* 25.8, http://apologeticspress.org/apPubPage.aspx?pub=1&issue=568&article=569.

Neither a pine tree nor a pinecone is sentient. They have no thinking capacity or consciousness. They possess no personhood, soul, or spirit. Pine trees did not get together and discuss the threat of forest fires to their future survival, and then decide to produce pinecones that would remain closed during a fire only to open afterwards. The standard explanations by evolutionists for such wonders of creation are incoherent and nonsensical . . . Only a foolish person would conclude there is no God (Psalm 14:1).

This is an intelligent man using an innovative and effective approach to natural theology. Christians need to employ this sort of creativity and knowledge in the arsenal of giving a reason for the hope that is in them. Adding this sort of technique in one's apologetic repertoire will enhance one's own faith while simultaneously helping activate the spiritual interests of an opponent.

Cooperation Between Sorghum And Bacteria

Seeing an example of design is captivating when witnessed in a single kingdom but what's even more captivating is when one sees cooperative design taking place across kingdoms. Evidence of this clearly occurs even the plant and bacteria kingdoms. This is exactly the case with respect to the popular grain Sorghum. Randy Guliuzza, P.E., M.D., has a thought-provoking article on how Sorghum intuitively adapts in drought conditions by manipulating soil conditions to benefit its

Figure 11.5 Sorghum

root microbiome.[191] He reviews a research study evolutionary biologists did on this very idea and critiques their misapprehension of design inherent to such a system. He posits that this is undeniable evidence that a designed communication channel of exceeding complexity exists between Sorghum and its bacteria, particularly with the Streptomyces strains of Actinobacteria. In his article, he writes,

The complex systems conferring such tight cooperation between plants and microbes point to a wise Creator for their origin far more reasonably than the mystical scenarios invoking strong "positive" and "negative" selection events of-

---

[191] Randy J. Guliuzza, "Sorghum and Bacteria Cooperative Design," Institute for Creation Research, http://www.icr.org/article/sorghum-and-bacteria-cooperative-design.

fered by the researchers . . . ICR research has shown that anytime two indepen- dent entities work together there must be an interface connecting them with a minimum of three elements: authentication mechanisms, regulatory protocols, and a common medium . . . a biblical explanation [of the interface between Sorghum and Actinobacteria, EP] is design-based and organismfocused and expects organisms to function according to engineering principles. We know that engineers may design one distinct entity like a radio to work together with another entity like a radio transmitter into a completely separate system called a communications system. An engineering-based explanation describing the relationships of microbes, plant, and animals would expect to find autonomous entities with innately designed adaptive capacities, entities that were originally designed to work together as parts of larger, non-violent, cooperative systems. These systems would yield results (some synergistic) that facilitate populations to continuously fill an ever-changing Earth just as they were commanded to do in Genesis 1:22, 28. Complex modes of adaptation work not only within the organism itself, but extend all the way out to interorganismal engineering that include bacteria and fungi working together with plant systems. This amazing co-engineering enables plants to optimally adapt to both temperature fluctua- tions and changes in soil water availability.

Cooperation Between the Yucca And Yucca Moth[192]

Cross-kingdom cooperation and communication is certainly a powerful testimony to a Programmer. Another case in which this is illustrated is in the sym- biosis of the yucca plant and the yucca moth. The yuc- ca plant is wholly incapable to pollinate itself in order to reproduce. The only way that it can is by directed pollination from yucca moths, which emerge from subterranean cocoons exactly when yuccas go into bloom! During this process, the yucca moths employ their singularly unique proboscis to gather pollen from the plant and then their ovipositor to place an egg in the ovary of another plant. Following this, they pollenate immature seeds at the tip of the pistil, which will be used as a food source for the hatchlings. If the balance were not fine-tuned, the extinction of both species would occur. What a clear testimony to their Programmer, Who demonstrates cooperation within the Father, Son, and Holy Spirit!

Figure 11.6 Yucca Moth

---

[192] "Yucca Moth," DesertUsa, https://www.desertusa.com/animals/yucca-moth.html.

These examples speak precious little on the powerful and plentiful testimony of symbiosis and mutualism that makes the most logical sense from a biblical creation standpoint rather than an evolutionary standpoint.[193] Truly, there are infinite subjects to be explored in the realm of biology! How exciting to be standing in the place that we are, where the pendulum of scientific vindication is swinging back toward the side of the believer!

The Animal Kingdom[194]

Sea Creatures And Birds

The Bible describes the creation of sea creatures and birds on the fifth day thus,

Figure 11.7 Cephalopoda

Then God said, "Let the waters teem with swarms of living creatures, and let birds fly above the earth in the open expanse of the heavens." God created the great sea monsters and every living creature that moves, with which the waters swarmed after their kind, and every winged bird after its kind; and God saw that it was good. God blessed them, saying, "Be fruitful and multiply, and fill the waters in the seas, and let birds multiply on the earth." There was evening and there was morning, a fifth day (Gen 1:20-23).

Among sea creatures, research among cephalopods has been perhaps the most challenging to the evolutionary paradigm. Squid, octopus, and cuttlefish genomes have revealed incredible rigidity unexplained by macroevolution.[195] These cephalopods have built in systems that fine tune their RNA molecules in ways unparalleled in other creatures. Without absolute DNA rigidity, this high functioning RNA editing would not be possible, thus ruling out evolutionary explanation. Octopi even have a special editing ability that allows them to live and thrive in a variety of environments and temperatures, despite limited nerve impulse speeds in colder environments.[196] The three aforementioned cephalopods are also able to flash bio-

---

[194] Many of these examples are sourced, as the plant examples were above, from the plethora of articles written by the writers of Apologetics Press as well as the Institute for Creation Research.

[195] Brian Thomas, "Squid, Octopus Genomes Alter Themselves, Blocking Evolution," Institute for Creation Research, http://www.icr.org/article/squid-octopus-genomes-alter-themselves.

luminescent colors across their skin through unique nerve networks, drastically differing even from the other cephalopods! These flashes, as well as other capabilities serve as sophisticated communications and camouflage systems unparalleled in human design and inspirations for biomimicry. These are real-life illustrations of an advanced Designer! Christians can use these examples to go toe-to-toe with naturalists, demolishing pseudo-intellectual strongholds with hard data.

Figure 11.8 Lobster

Another fascinating example of irreducible complexity is the dangerous molting process of lobsters.[197] During this process, many stages are absolutely vital in sequence or the crustacean would cease to survive. Among these elements is the lobster's intentional and essential water intake to the tune of adding ten percent body weight prior to, during, and immediately following ecdysis (i.e. molting). Also, during proecdysis (i.e. premolting), new limbs are even formed that had been amputated!

Another example of the sea, the purple sea urchin, has been shown to demonstrate the ability to overcome increased acidity in a laboratory setting. Evolutionary scientists have misused this finding to prop up their theory, but rather than being a novel innovated development as these scientists suggest, the urchin seems to have already possessed this capability as a part of its own programming.[198] Tracing this history and revealing its origin provides a successful bio-cosmological argument.

Turning our attention to birds, mankind instinctively knows that God exists because of these creatures. Man has yearned to fly for as long as man could dream. In today's world, we see that dream realized. Men can fly across the world in less than a day. Thousands of miles are traversed with food service, movies, and Wi-Fi. Yet, who would deny that man's imitation of birds and flying insects is cheap in comparison? The efficiency, beauty, and streamlined flight of everything from an osprey to a hummingbird make Airbus pale in comparison. In fact, history's greatest pioneers of flight, the Wright Brothers, repeatedly spoke of being inspired by

---

[196] Brian Thomas, "Octopus Cold Adaptation Surprises Scientists," Institute for Creation Research, http://www.icr.org/article/octopus-cold-adaptation-surprises-scientists.

[197] James J.S. Johnson, "Lobsters Get Comfortable in Their New Skin," Institute for Creation Research, http://www.icr.org/article/lobsters-get-comfortable-in-their-new-skin.

[198] Brian Thomas, "Spiny Sea Creature Rapidly Accommodates Chemical Changes," Institute for Creation Research, http://www.icr.org/article/spiny-sea-creature-rapidly-accommodates.

Figure 11.9 Purple Sea Urchins

God's creation and design of birds. Their bioinspiration came from their observation in nature and, specifically, the fifty-three mentions of birds in the Scriptures.[199] Technological pioneering finds origin in man's study of created beings that bear God's fingerprints!

Bioinspiration for flight also comes from dragonflies and other species whose flight patterns and capabilities engineers and fighter pilots can only dream of.[200] One creationist writes,

If scores of intelligent scientists must expend vast amounts of time, energy, intention, deliberation, knowledge, and thought in order to discover the secrets of the "efficient motions" of the dragonfly, what must have been required to create that dragonfly in the first place? Mindless, non-intelligent, unconscious, non-purposive "evolutionary forces"? Ridiculous! Time and chance do not and cannot account for the amazing design found in insects like the dragonfly. The only logical, plausible explanation is that dragonflies were designed by the God of the Bible, and they testify to His wisdom: "You are worthy, O Lord, to receive glory and honor and power; for You created all things, and by Your will they exist and were created" (Revelation 4:11).[201]

Figure 11.10 Bald Eagle

Although taxonomically more related to insects (discussed below), bees are flying creatures as well so let's take a minute in this section to think about some of

---

[199] For more detail on this story of inspiration, see: Jerry Bergman, "Bioinspiration: The Birds Will Tell You," Institute for Creation Research, http://www.icr.org/article/bioinspiration-birds-will-tell-you; Jerry Fausz, "Designed To Fly," Reason and Revelation 28.2, http://apologeticspress.org/APPubPage.aspx?pub=1&issue=598&section=0&article=688&cat=328.

[200] Jerry Fausz, "Morphing Flight: Beyond Irreducible Complexity," Reason and Revelation 30.1, http://apologeticspress.org/APPubPage.aspx?pub=1&issue=621&section=0&article=448&cat=328.

[201] Dave Miller, "Dragonfly Flight and the Designer," Reason and Revelation 26.4, http://apologeticspress.org/APPubPage.aspx?pub=1&issue=576&section=0&article=607&cat=328.

the biological marvels observed in bees. Bees are famous for their ability to communicate with other bees through complex dance routines. More recent research has also shown that, despite their miniature brain size, their ability to comprehend, analyze, and even maintain a biological clock is more akin to humans than to most other insects. Various studies have shown this extraordinary cognitive malleability.[202] The marvelous flight and landing abilities of bees and hummingbirds have likewise been a source of bioinspiration. [203] [204] [205] God's wisdom and craftiness are at the root of flight (cf. Job 39:26). Evolutionary "explanations" fall flat.[206]

With respect to flight, birds are notoriously powerful examples in the area of migration, a subject addressed in the Scriptures thousands of years ago (Jer 8:7)! Without compass, map, or GPS, they fly in huge amounts in short periods without stopping for food, water, or rest. They must clearly be programmed and designed to do this. Eric Lyons, in an article already cited above, gives one such example:

> In February 2007, scientists from the U.S. Geological Survey fitted 16 shore-birds, known as bar-tailed godwits, with satellite transmitters. One of the godwits, dubbed E7, made its way from New Zealand to Alaska over the next three months, flying 9,340 miles with one five-week-long layover near the North Korea-China border (Hansford, 2007). After nearly four months, the godwit began its uninterrupted flight back to New Zealand. Amazingly, this little bird, which normally weighs less than one pound, flew 7,145 miles in nine days without stopping, averaging 34.8 mph. Without taking a break to eat, drink, or rest, the godwit flew "the equivalent of making a roundtrip flight between New York and San Francisco, and then flying back again to San Francisco without ever touching down" ("Bird Completes...," 2007). Equally impressive, the

---

[202] Frank Sherwin, "Bees Are Actually Really, Really, Really Smart," Institute for Creation Research, http://www.icr.org/article/bees-really-smart.

[203] Bioinspiration with regards to flight is also seen in research on the flight and landing patterns of bees, which shames our best technologies. See: Brian Thomas, "Bee Landing Strategy May Lead to Better Aircraft," Institute for Creation Research, http://www.icr.org/article/bee-landing-strategy-may-lead-better.

[204] Ironically, scientists formerly called honeybee flight "impossible." After more research, the honeybee's methods of flight were found to be intentional and well suited for its particular needs. See: Dave Miller, "Bee Flight Physics," Reason and Revelation 26.2, http://apologeticspress.org/APPubPage.aspx?pub=1&issue=574&section=0&article=443&cat=328.

[205] Kyle Butt, "Robotic Hummingbirds Defies Evolution," Reason and Revelation 31.5, http://apologeticspress.org/APPubPage.aspx?pub=1&issue=970&section=0&article=1484&cat=328.

[206] Jerry Fausz, "Response to 'Insect Wing Evolution Revealed in Recycled Genes,'" Reason and Revelation, 30.6, http://apologeticspress.org/APPubPage.aspx?pub=1&issue=923&section=0&article=1412&cat=328.

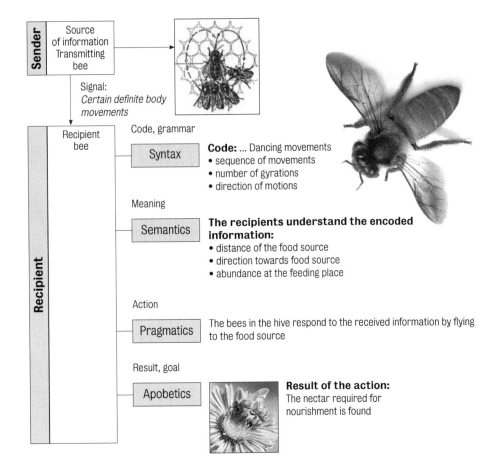

Figure 11.11   Bee Communication Via Dancing

godwit's approximately 16,500-mile, roundtrip journey ended where it began. Without a map, a compass, or even a parent, godwits can fly tens of thousands of miles without getting lost.[207]

Cattle, Creeping Things, And Beasts of the Earth

On the sixth day of creation, God created the major and diverse groups of cattle, creeping things, and beasts of the earth:

Then God said, "Let the earth bring forth living creatures after their kind: cat-

[207] Lyons cites the following two works in his quote: Hansford, Dave Hansford, "Alaska Bird Makes Longest Nonstop Flight Ever Measured," *National Geographic News*, http://news.nationalgeographic.com/news/2007/09/070913-longest-flight.html; and also, "Bird Completes Epic Flight Across the Pacific," *ScienceDaily*, http://www.sciencedaily.com/releases/2007/09/070915131 205. htm.

tle and creeping things and beasts of the earth after their kind"; and it was so. God made the beasts of the earth after their kind, and the cattle after their kind, and everything that creeps on the ground after its kind; and God saw that it was good (Gen 1:24-25).

The Bible's taxonomy in Gen 1 and elsewhere is not as detailed as what taxonomists use today, but, obviously, one of the applications of "creeping things" would include insects. Insects are incredible little creatures of resilience, adaptability, and they also bear the indelible impression of their Fabricator. Their sudden existence in all their various kinds, as well as a substantive gap in the fossil record (called the "hexapod gap") only reasonably explained by Noah's Flood, gives powerful testimony through the facts of science that God is the Creator and Designer and Programmer.

Figure 11.12   Diamond Weevil

A major subject of discussion for many biologists in recent years has been weevils.[208] Diamond and glossy rainbow weevils in particular have recently been studied in an effort to understand their body's elegant and efficient photonic structures. Researchers have realized that these structures are optimally coordinated for light reflectance in a way that far exceeds human designs. Optimal sorts of photonic structures have also been studied in butterflies as well. These studies have proven so helpful that engineers are attempting to harness this optimal design for artificial photonic materials! Sadly though, the researchers in many studies like these honor the mindless process of macroevolution, which fails to possess any explanatory power for such structures. As we noted in our chapter on information, structures like these are packed with information and coding wholly unexplained by naturalistic processes, yet fully explained in every instance by observational examples of design and mind.

Another fascinating area of study is how insects and arachnids survive in higher latitudes and colder climates. James J.S. Johnson, J.D., TH.D., asks and answers this question:

How can insects and arachnids withstand frigid forces of frost and freezing? The answer highlights a strong apologetics argument for creation. Evolution-

---

[208] Two examples include: Brian Thomas, "Diamond Weevil Studded with Advanced Technology," Institute for Creation Research, http://www.icr.org/article/diamond-weevil-studded-with-advanced; and Jeffrey P. Tomkins, "Complex Engineering in Weevils Befuddles Evolution," Institute for Creation Research, http://www.icr.org/article/complex-engineering-weevil.

ists are routinely guilty of the oversimplification fallacy, as if creature survival traits implement "one size fits all" simplicity. The opposite is true—God loves variety and intricate details, so don't be surprised when He employs diverse problem-solving strategies to overcome the same problem. With careful bioengineering (including environmental tracking programming), God has providentially prepared multi-legged creepy critters with five very different solutions to avoid being fatally frozen.

Johnson goes on to list these five ways as: habitat selection, migration, hibernation-like freeze avoidance, "antifreeze," and freeze tolerance. After explaining the marvel of each of these options, he concludes:

How would beetles evolve these magnificent adaptabilities, phenologically indexed to Earth's annual temperature and photoperiodicity rhythms? There is no way that random mutations accidently "emerging" along insect or spider genomes could ever program bug physiologies to so successfully fill super-cold habitats. As a matter of cold logic and biochemistry, these super-cool critters can't be lucky products of evolutionary magic. They instead demonstrate God's creatorship![209]

Biological systems utilized for vision and compensation for vision insufficiency or loss point to a Designer as well. Many mammals such as bats, dolphins, orca whales, and beluga whales use a form of auditory sight known as

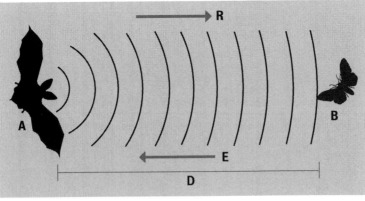

Above,
Figure 11.13
Blind
Cave Fish

Left,
Figure 11.14
Echolocation

---

[209] James J.S. Johnson, "Withstanding Winter Weather," Institute for Creation Research, http://www.icr.org/article/withstanding-winter-weather.

Figure 11.15 Common Shrew

echolocation, a natural and better version of sonar. This helps these animals navigate in dark and cluttered areas without causing injury or even death. Although belonging in the taxonomy prior to this section, mantis shrimp have an amazing vision capability as well. Their tiny eyes contain four times the photoreceptors of humans and they use amino acids to function as sunblock, thus allowing them to view on the ultraviolet spectrum![210] Likewise, blind cave fish have been shown to develop other senses (particularly taste and touch) to compensate for their loss of vision so that they can still "see." Even shrews, one of the smallest mammals, have increased their sense of touch via whiskers to compensate for poor vision! All of these, in addition to the animals that have extraordinary focusing ability and clarity from the start without relying on supplementary systems (e.g. eagles, peregrine falcons, owls, sheep, goats, etc.), point to a Designer that Canon, Nikon, and Olympus cannot hold a candle to!

One last example to consider is the tallest land animal—the giraffe. As lanky and clumsy as this massive creature seems, it can run up to 34 mph and walks between thirty minutes to an hour after birth. In ten hours, these six-foot tall infants are able to run and keep pace with the herd. Giraffes hardly ever sleep too, only a total of thirty minutes per day broken up into a few power naps. This oddball creature can also go weeks without drinking, making it ideally suited for its primary habitat in the savanna regions of sub-Saharan Africa. Eric Lyons has a helpful discussion on perhaps the greatest example of design in giraffes—their circulatory system. He discusses tailor-made elements in this system that allow the giraffe to pump blood against gravity the massive distance from the heart to brain, maintain cranial blood pressure despite drastic changes in position above and below the heart, epithelial tissue thick and sturdy enough

Figure 11.16 Giraffe

[210] Kyle Butt, "Seeing the Designer in Shrimp Vision," Reason and Revelation 34.9, http://apologeticspress.org/APPubPage.aspx?pub=1&issue=1172&section=0&article=2438&cat=328.

to abide the high blood pressure necessary for this creature to live, and oversized lungs to allow compensation for the "dead space" in the gargantuan neck of these creatures.[211]

Concluding Thought:
The Importance of Biological Marvels For Christians

While some of the examples above are irreducibly complex and some may not be, they are nonetheless telling of a Designer. They bear that signature of design that we spoke of in an earlier chapter; there is information and programming clearly evident in these highly advanced systems! Keep in mind that the examples above are non-exhaustive! We have given a meager portion of the adaptability that God has programmed into His biological systems.[212]

The reason this discussion is so crucial is because the Bible repeatedly attests to the fact that God is witnessed in creation. Christians need to feel confident in the knowledge that God is observable in the world today and that His ability to be seen in the world is something that mankind willfully chooses to suppress. As Rom 1:18-25 reads,

For the wrath of God is revealed from heaven against all ungodliness and unrighteousness of men who suppress the truth in unrighteousness, because that which is known about God is evident within them; for God made it evident to them. For since the creation of the world His invisible attributes, His eternal power and divine nature, have been clearly seen, being understood through what has been made, so that they are without excuse. For even though they knew God, they did not honor Him as God or give thanks, but they became futile in their speculations, and their foolish heart was darkened. Professing to be wise, they became fools, and exchanged the glory of the incorruptible God for an image in the form of corruptible man and of birds and four-footed animals and crawling creatures. Therefore God gave them over in the lusts of their hearts to impurity, so that their bodies would be dishonored among them. For they exchanged the truth of God for a lie, and worshiped and served the creature rather than the Creator, who is blessed forever. Amen.

---

[211] Eric Lyons, "Wonders of God's Creation," *Reason and Revelation* 29.1, http://apologeticspress.org/APPubPage.aspx?pub=1&issue=609&section=0&article=722&cat=328.

[212] Dr. Randy J. Guliuzza, P.E., MD, has an excellent series of seventeen different articles examining this programmed adaptability and why evolution cannot explain it. He also gives powerful positive testimony to God's design of these features as well. The series is entitled "Engineered Adaptability" and can be found on the ICR website.

Having this assurance makes evangelism and apologetics much easier, especially in the face of persecution and rejection (1 Cor 15:58). Christians studying and employed in assorted fields of science need to especially remain strong and not become fearful so as to give credence to falsehood. Christians also need to remember that God created man in His image (Gen 1:26-27), set eternity in the heart of man (Eccl 3:11), and left Himself thorough witness (Acts 14:17). Therefore, man's rejection is a sin problem, a problem that will be exposed in the next and final chapter of our book. We close this chapter with one last quote from Dave Miller:

Do cars just happen? Of course not. Their multiple systems are interactive and integrated with each other in order for the automobile to operate. A mind—no, multiple minds—lie behind the creation of a car. Yet, compared to the Universe, or compared to the human body, or even compared to the inner workings of one tree leaf, a car is a crude and primitive invention. If the creation of a car demands the existence of the remarkable human brain/mind, what must be required for the creation of the human brain/mind? Obviously, something or Someone far superior to the human mind would be needed for its creation. Logically, that Someone must be the powerful, transcendent Creator: the God of the Bible. The naturalistic explanation given by evolutionists for the existence of the created order cannot meet the dictates of logic that characterize the unencumbered, unprejudiced human mind. The more one investigates the intricacies and complexities of the natural realm, the more self-evident it is that a grand and great Designer is responsible for the existence of the Universe. In fact, the evidence is overwhelming and decisive.[213]

---

[213] Dave Miller, "The Teleological Argument for the Existence of God [Part 1]," *Reason and Revelation* 38.2, http://apologeticspress.org/APPubPage.aspx?pub=1&issue=1264&section=0&article=2774&cat=329.

Thought Questions:

1. What is teleology?

_____

_____

_____

_____

2. Does the Bible argue for God from the standpoint of ID and/or irreducible complexity?

_____

_____

_____

_____

3. What does the Bible say about migratory patterns?

_____

_____

_____

_____

4. What is your favorite biological marvel discussed in this chapter?

_____

_____

_____

_____

5. What sort of witness has the Lord given for Himself? (Acts 14:17)

_____

_____

_____

_____

CHAPTER 12

An Uphill Battle

Why a "Scientific Mind" May Still Resist this Evidence

The information in this volume constitutes a powerful scientific argument for God. And this is only a fraction of the evidence available! Exploring these avenues of thought is very faith building and faith affirming, isn't it? Who would deny that belief in God is reasonable and scientifically tenable in light of this evidence? Who would deny that evolution and other less popular forms of materialistic philosophy are impotent in light of such reasoning?[214]

The great Baptist commentator Charles Spurgeon declares, "*Nothing is easi-*

"When I consider Your heavens, the work of Your fingers, The moon and the stars, which You have ordained; What is man that You take thought of him, And the son of man that You care for him?" Psalm 8:3-4

Figure 12.1

---

[214] The late botanist Dr. Herbert Nilsson is spot on when he states in his book *The Synthetic Formation of Kinds*, "*The final result of all my researches and discussions is that the theory of evolution should be discarded in its entirety, because it always leads to extreme contradictions and confusing consequences when tested against the empirical results of research on the formation of different kinds of living forms and related fields. This assertion would agitate many people. Moreover: my next conclusion is that, far from being a benign naturalphilosophical school of though, the theory of evolution is a severe obstacle for biological research. As many examples show, it actually prevents the drawing of logical conclusions from even one set of experimental material. Because everything must be bent to fit this speculative theory, an exact biology cannot develop.*"

er than doubting. A poorly educated person with mediocre abilities can raise more doubts than can be resolved by the cleverest men of science from all over the world.[215] In other words, sadly, you could make a perfectly sound and logical argument and there would still be plenty of critics who remain unconvinced. So, why does this happen? In a word, sin. But let's explore several specific issues that contribute to this.

Intellectual Issues

One of the cleverest beings in the entire universe is Satan. He is an adversary whose knowledge is unmatched, with singular exception to God. Satan is crafty and scheming, downright diabolical. One of his greatest resources is deception, and he is exceptionally skilled at intellectual duplicity. Daily, he foments confusion and ruse; hourly he strokes cerebral egos. The Bible issues memorable warnings with regard to this tactic of Satan and the danger of solely relying on intellect.

Woe to those who are wise in their own eyes and clever in their own sight! (Isa 5:21).

For the word of the cross is foolishness to those who are perishing, but to us who are being saved it is the power of God. For it is written, "I will destroy the wisdom of the wise, And the cleverness of the clever I will set aside."

Where is the wise man? Where is the scribe? Where is the debater of this age? Has not God made foolish the wisdom of the world? For since in the wisdom of God the world through its wisdom did not come to know God, God was wellpleased through the foolishness of the message preached to save those who believe. For indeed Jews ask for signs and Greeks search for wisdom; but we preach Christ crucified, to Jews a stumbling block and to Gentiles foolishness, but to those who are the called, both Jews and Greeks, Christ the power of God and the wisdom of God. Because the foolishness of God is wiser than men, and the weakness of God is stronger than men. For consider your calling, brethren, that there were not many wise according to the flesh, not many mighty, not many noble; but God has chosen the foolish things of the world to shame the wise, and God has chosen the weak things of the world to shame the things which are strong, and the base things of the world and the despised God has chosen, the things that are not, so that He may nullify the things that are, so that no man may boast before God. But by His doing you are in Christ Jesus, who became to us wisdom from God, and righteousness and sanctification,

---

[215] Quoted in Werner Gitt, *In the Beginning Was Information: A Scientist Explains the Incredible Design in Nature* (Green Forest, AR: Masters Books, 2007), 162.

and redemption, so that, just as it is written, "Let him who boasts, boast in the Lord" (1 Cor 1:18-31).

If anyone supposes that he knows anything, he has not yet known as he ought to know; but if anyone loves God, he is known by Him (1 Cor 8:2-3).

Therefore let him who thinks he stands take heed that he does not fall (1 Cor 10:12).

And He gave some as apostles, and some as prophets, and some as evangelists, and some as pastors and teachers, for the equipping of the saints for the work of service, to the building up of the body of Christ; until we all attain to the unity of the faith, and of the knowledge of the Son of God, to a mature man, to the measure of the stature which belongs to the fullness of Christ. As a result, we are no longer to be children, tossed here and there by waves and carried about by every wind of doctrine, by the trickery of men, by craftiness in deceitful scheming; but speaking the truth in love, we are to grow up in all aspects into Him who is the head, even Christ, from whom the whole body, being fitted and held together by what every joint supplies, according to the proper working of each individual part, causes the growth of the body for the building up of itself in love (Eph 4:11-16).

To these warnings could be added multitudes more.

Let's consider what scientists have to say about the intellectual obstacles resulting from Satan's handiwork. Michael Denton describes the issue not quite from a believer's standpoint (as he is a self-declared agnostic) but clearly opposed to an evolutionary standpoint. He says that scientists *"will go to extraordinary length. . . to defend a theory just as long as it holds scientific intrinsic appeal."* Dr. D.M.S. Watson, the late zoologist of London University illustrates intellectual blockades erected by Satan when he candidly admits *"Evolution is a theory universally accepted, not because it can be proved true, but because the only alternative, Special Creation, is clearly impossible."*[216] Evidently, then, the issue is not a lack of observable evidence but rather an a priori dismissal of the possibility of God, a tactic whose origin is in Satan.

Emotional Issues

Many scientific minds will admit the information available leans heavily toward the Christian apologist's side. Still, they refuse to yield because of the implications.

---

[216] D.M.S. Watson, "Adaptation," *Nature* 124:233, 1929.

These persons illustrate emotional issues with the fact of God's existence.
Shame, fear, embarrassment, ridicule,
and a host of other emotional obstacles
are enough to prevent such persons
from commitment to the Lord, despite
the evidence. If only they would allow
themselves to be perfected in the love
of Christ, fear of all forms of judgment
would lose its gripping power (cf. 1
John 4:18). Let's consider illustrations
of this type of issue from a variety of
perspectives in the scientific community.

Figure 12.2

Joseph Pilbeam openly and fearfully admits the available scientific information
is totally antagonistic to naturalist viewpoints while still futilely clinging to evolutionary biology. He writes in a review of Mary Leakey's *Origins*,

> *My reservations concern not so much this book but the whole subject of paleo-
> anthropology. But introductory books—or book reviews—are hardly the place
> to argue that perhaps generations of students of human evolution, including
> myself, have been flailing about in the dark: that our data base is too sparse,
> too slippery, for it to be able to mold our theories. Rather the theories are more
> statements about us and ideology than about the past. Paleoanthropology re-
> veals more about how humans view themselves than it does about how hu-
> mans came about. But that is heresy.*[217]

Satan has done his work well! Scientists, who are alleged to go into and operate
in their field with objectivity are clearly and admittedly not objective! Why and
how does this happen? Dr. Bo Kirkwood, a devout believer in God explains how
intellectual and emotional commitments muddy the water:

> *"Of course there are many who accept evolution simply because they do not
> know any better. It is shoved down their throats in school, and to oppose it can
> become quite uncomfortable. They will be ridiculed and told that only theb
> ignorant or deluded do not accept evolution, and who wants to appear stupid
> or crazy!"*[218]

---

[217] Pilbeam's review of Leaky's *Origins in American Scientific,* May-June, 1978.

[218] Bo Kirkwood, *Creation Versus Evolution* (Athens, AL: Truth Publications, 2017), 71-72.

Terry Mortenson, PhD History of Geology, reveals the root of the matter to be fear of accountability. He states, *"It's not a battle between religion and science; it's a battle over authority. These individuals are trying to explain the world without God so they don't have to be morally accountable to Him."*[219]

Will Issues

We stated earlier that the fundamental issue is sin. While issues of the intellect and emotions contribute, the main issue is a matter of the will or volition. After all, that is the end of the intellectual and emotional reasons and excuses. Truly, rejection of God is a matter of choice; a choice rooted in stubbornness, pride, and idolatry. God openly calls men to *"Cease striving and know that I am God!"* (Ps 46:10). Oh, if men would only cease the futile resistance! The reality of God is so blindingly obvious! Dr. Bo Kirkwood strikes this chord when he writes,

> *Most will not accept creation simply because they just can't! They hold a nat-uralistic viewpoint and cannot entertain the supernatural, no matter what evidence they are shown. Since they cannot accept creation, they are therefore blinded by evolution . . . But when one accepts the possibility of creation, the evidence for it is overwhelming."*[220]

Sadly, though, choice is a powerful gift, and Satan does all he can to pervert this gift in his favor. Let's consider several pitiable confessions of rebellious wills that have become subjected to Satan's burden-some yoke.

> *It necessarily follows that chance alone is at the source of every innovation, and of all creation in the biosphere. Pure chance, absolutely free but blind, at the very root of the stupendous edifice of evolution:*

Figure 12.3
Jacques Monod

> *this central concept of modern biology is no longer one among many other possible or even conceivable hypotheses. It is today the sole conceivable hypothesis, the only one that squares with observed and tested fact. And nothing warrants the supposition— or the hope—that on this score our position is ever likely to be revised.*[221]

---

[219] Terry Mortenson, PhD History of Geology in: The New Answers 1, DVD, directed by Ben Wilt (Hebron, KY: Answers in Genesis, 2009).

[220] Kirkwood, *Creation Versus Evolution*, 70.

[221] Jacques Monod, *Chance And Necessity* (New York: Vintage Books, 1971), 112-113.

We take the side of science in spite of the patent absurdity of some of the constructs. In spite of its failure to fulfill many of its extravagant promises of health and life, in spite of the tolerance of the scientific community for unsubstantiated just-so stories, because we have a prior commitment, a commitment to materialism. It is not that the methods and intuitions of science somehow compel us to accept a natural explanation of the phenomenal world, but on the contrary, we are forced by our prior adherence to natural causes to create an apparatus of investigation and a set of concepts that produce that materialism is absolute, for we cannot allow a Divine Foot in the door.[222]

The fundamental truth of biological evolution is accepted beforehand, yes, we assume in advance that the principle of evolution is universally valid, that it is just as valid in the pre-organic domain as in the organic, and that it can be extended to the spheres of psychology, sociology, and culture. If we accept that the evolutionary view also holds for the human mind and cognition, then evolutionary ideas can also be applied to the analysis of those phenomena which are usually regarded as belonging to theoretical science. As a result this view then becomes relatively more important in the evaluation of the progress of scientific research. We thus arrive at an evolutionary theory of science, a theory of human knowledge which relates to an evolutionary establishment of itself.[223]

If [God] does exist, I personally want nothing to do with him.[224]

I want atheism to be true and am made uneasy by the fact that some of the most intelligent and well-informed people I know are religious believers. It isn't just that I don't believe in God and, naturally, hope that I'm right in my belief. It's that I hope there is no God! I don't want there to be a God; I don't want the universe to be like that.[225]

Figure 12.4
Victor Stenger

The reason we accepted Darwinism even without proof, is because we didn't want God to interfere with our sexual mores.[226]

[222] Richard Lewontin, "Billions and Billions of Demons" (review of *The Demon-Haunted World: Science as a Candle in the Dark* by Carl Sagan, 1997), *The New York Review*, p. 31, 9 January 1997.

[223] Franz M. Wuketits quoted in: Werner Gitt, *In the Beginning Was Information: A Scientist Explains the Incredible Design in Nature* (Green Forest, AR: Master Books, 2007), 100.

[224] Victor Stenger, *God: The Failed Hypothesis* (New York: Prometheus Books, 2007), 240.

[225] Thomas Nagel, *The Last Word* (New York: Oxford University Press, 1997), 130-131.

We no longer feel ourselves to be guests in someone else's home and therefore obligated to make our behavior conform with a set of preexisting cosmic rules. It is our creation now. We make the rules. We establish the parameters of reality. We create the world, and because we do, we no longer feel beholden to outside forces. We no longer have to justify our behavior, for we are now the architects of the universe. We are responsible to nothing outside ourselves, for we are the kingdom, the power, and the glory forever and ever.[227]

Figure 12.5
Thomas Nagel

What straightforward admissions! Science, far from being objective, has become so saturated with atheistic philosophy that being a scientist and being a believer has become a hostile environment! Sadly, rebellious and callous wills, bases of operation for the Adversary, have effectively intellectually marginalized Christians. Rather than being enlightened and free, these have become futile in mind and excluded from the life of God; these are ignorant and calloused, wholly devoted to impurity and self-aggrandizement (Eph 4:17-19). These have seared in their minds and consciences as with a branding iron (1 Tim 4:1-5). As the preacher pinpointed, *"God made man upright, but they have sought out many schemes"* (Eccl 7:29). Satan has blinded the minds of these unbelievers (2 Cor 4:3-4).

Figure 12.6
Julian Huxley

So How Should We Respond?

Effective, informed response is necessary. But given admissions like those above, the task seems insufferable. If people refuse to listen, why even try?

While frustrations abound, there are some who nevertheless are convinced by the evidence. There are those whose faith was flagging but examination of the evidence bolstered them. It works! It may not work as often as Christians would like, but it works! God may also be using Christians and their apologetic to harden further! It very well may be that your job is to "put a rock in someone's shoe." God knew from the start that Pharaoh would not respond (Exod 4:21); nonetheless, Moses preaches to him! God's encouragement of Ezekiel (Ezek 3:4-9) is even clearer and inspiring:

---

[226] Julian Huxley in an interview on *The Merv Griffin Show* in the late 1960s. Quoted in Giesler and Turek, *I Don't Have Enough Faith to Be an Atheist*, 163.

[227] Jeremy Rifkin, *Algeny* (New York: Viking Press, 1983), 244.

Then He said to me, "Son of man, go to the house of Israel and speak with My words to them. For you are not being sent to a people of unintelligible speech or difficult language, but to the house of Israel, nor to many peoples of unintelligible speech or difficult language, whose words you cannot understand. But I have sent you to them who should listen to you; yet the house of Israel will not be willing to listen to you, since they are not willing to listen to Me. Surely the whole house of Israel is stubborn and obstinate. Behold, I have made your face as hard as their faces and your forehead as hard as their foreheads. Like emery harder than flint I have made your forehead. Do not be afraid of them or be dismayed before them, though they are a rebellious house."

Figure 12.7 Michelangelo's Ezekiel, Sistine Chapel

Providing an apologetic is the responsibility of all Christians, young and old (1 Pet 3:15). Christians must do this, "knowing that [their labor] is not in vain" (1 Cor 15:58). This requires speaking on the level of the requestor. Imagine if Paul had not spoken to the Athenians in their own terms by quoting their own philosophers. His effectiveness would have been reduced. This in no way undermines the effectiveness of the gospel to convert; rather, in using the resources God has given us, we effectively present the gospel to others in terms they will consider. The power, as always, is in the gospel (Rom 1:16).

We might add that equipping oneself for this defense of the faith holds treasures of benefits.[228] We see personal, familial, and collective benefits from this sort of development. We are constantly bombarded with the notion that we have to adjust our views to catch up with the fact. This is a deception. How helpful to apprehend that what we see in God's world agrees with what we see in God's Word! Analysis of evidence in the light of God's Word will increase our faith and make us sharper implements for the hand of God. This growth is a command of God! Furthermore, the pursuit of science is a unique expression of being made in God's image. It is important for Christians to pursue science. Paleontologist Kurt Wise highlights this truth: *"Science is a means of better understanding God's creation so that we can serve Him by meeting the needs of that creation."*[229]

---

[228] *"A man has joy in an apt answer, / And how delightful is a timely word!"* (Prov 15:23).

Final Summation

Does science prove the Bible wrong? Have we evolved beyond the fictitious belief in God in light of cold hard facts? Is Nietzsche correct in declaring, "God is dead"? Is Freud right in asserting that "God" is a mere projection of a psyche broken by daddy issues? Much of the scientific community would tell us yes, this is precisely the case. However, this by no means represents all of the scientific community. There are many scientists working in their respective fields who see clear evidence for God. These men and women are gifted and they are ardent in showing agreement between science and the Bible.

While it can be intimidating to learn enough of this sort of information to provide an informed response to a critic of the Bible, it is important that we do so. Countless souls have been deluded, deceived, and misled and have Hell as a reward. Many of those are our loved ones. Perhaps even you have fallen prey to this deception. We hope that you will heed the information available in God's <u>natural</u> revelation AND in His <u>special</u> revelation.

I hope that this book has been helpful for you. I have thoroughly enjoyed affirming my own faith and hopefully affirming your faith. Perhaps this book has put you in a more intimate space with God. We would be grateful for that. God is indeed real. Heaven and Hell are real. Sin and salvation are real. Judgment and resurrection are real. We hope that conviction of your spirit will lead you to repent of your sins and take up your cross and follow after the resurrected Savior Jesus Christ.

We offer one final observation from Warren Wiersbe:

Figure 12.8   Michelangelo's Creation of Adam, Sistine Chapel

---

[229] Is Genesis History?, DVD, directed by Thomas Purifoy, Jr. (Newtown, PA: Virgil Films, 2017).

True saving faith isn't just a feat of intellectual gymnastics by which we convince ourselves that something is true that really isn't true. Nor is it merely a stirring of emotions that gives us a false sense or confidence that God will do what we feel He will do. Nor is it a courageous act of the will whereby we jump off the pinnacle of the temple and expect God to rescue us. True saving faith involves the whole personality: the mind is instructed, the emotions are stirred, and the will then acts in obedience to God.[230]

---

[230] Warren W. Wiersbe, Be Strong: *Putting God's Power to Work in Your Life* (Colorado Springs: David C. Cook, 2010), 49.

Thought Questions:

1. If Christians gave a perfect apologetic (scientific or otherwise) for Christianity, would every atheist and agnostic be converted? Why or why not?

2. What intellectual issues create a barrier between people and God?

3. What emotional issues create a barrier between people and God?

4. What will issues create a barrier between people and God?

5. In light of these obstacles, why should Christians still study the areas of apologetics discussed in this book?

Credits & Permissions

Figure 1.1: Inherit the Wind screenshot courtesy of Wikimedia Commons / Public Domain.

Figure 1.2: School of Athens by Raphael courtesy of Shutterstock.

Figure 1.3: Scientist image courtesy of User: Jiri Navratil / Wikimedia Commons / CC BY-SA-4.0. Used with permission; usage not intended to imply endorsement by the author/licensor of the work.

Figure 1.4: Photograph of cover of Darwin's Doubt taken by the author.

Figure 1.5: G.K. Chesterton image courtesy of Wikimedia Commons / Public Domain.

Figure 1.6: Photograph of cover of The Chronicles of Narnia, The Magician's Nephew taken by the author.

Figure 2.1: Francis Bacon image courtesy of Wikimedia Commons / Public Domain.

Figure 2.2: Creation versus the Big Bang chart created by Stephen Sebree using images taken from Shutterstock.

Figure 2.3: Dominoes image courtesy of Pixabay / Public Domain.

Figure 2.4: Fingerprint over world image courtesy of Pixabay / Public Domain.

Figure 2.5: Image of Louis Pasteur taken by Paul Nadar / Courtesy of Wikimedia Commons / Public Domain.

Figure 2.6: Mountaintop image courtesy of Pixabay / Public Domain.

Figure 2.7: Brain image courtesy of Shutterstock.

Figure 2.8: World in hand image courtesy of Shutterstock.

Figure 3.1: Geological time spiral image redrawn by Stephen Sebree based on information from Graham, Joseph, Newman, William, and Stacy, John, 2008, The geologic time spiral—A path to the past (ver. 1.1): U.S. Geological Survey General Information Product 58, poster, 1 sheet. Available online at http://pubs.usgs.gov/gip/2008/58. Public Domain.

Figure 3.2: Photograph of Francis Crick courtesy of Marc Lieberman / Wikimedia Commons / CC BY-SA-2.5. Used with permission; usage not intended to imply endorsement by the author/licensor of the work.

Figure 3.3: Photograph of the Grand Canyon courtesy of Shutterstock.

Figure 3.4: Before and after images of Mount St. Helens eruption courtesy of Harry Glicken / U.S. Geological Survey, Department of the Interior / CC BY-SA-2.0. Used with permission; usage not intended to imply endorsement by the author/licensor of the work.

Figure 3.5: Photograph of Terry Mortenson courtesy of Answers in Genesis.

Figure 3.6: Photograph of Andrew Snelling courtesy of Answers in Genesis.

Figure 4.1: Nile Mosaic of Palestrina image courtesy of Palestrina Nile Mosaic / Stockafisso / Shutterstock.com.

Figure 4.2: Dinosaur timeline drawn by Stephen Sebree.

Figure 4.3: Marco Polo portrait from Palazzo Tursi courtesy of Wikimedia Commons / Public Domain.

Figure 4.4: Image of Pliny the Elder courtesy of Courtesy of the National Institutes of Health, Department of Health and Human Services / Public Domain.

Figure 4.5: Image of Herodotus bust courtesy of User: Marie-Lan Nguyen / Wikimedia Commons / CC BY-SA-2.5. Used with permission; usage not intended to imply endorsement by the author/licensor of the work.

Figure 4.6: Image of Shunosaurus fossil from China courtesy of Steve Rudd. Used with permission.

Figure 4.7: Gryposaurus image redrawn by Stephen Sebree based on information granted by Genesis Park.

Figure 4.8: Burdick Track image courtesy of Steve Rudd. Used with permission.

Figure 4.9: Dinosaur art from Utah courtesy of Steve Rudd. Used with permission.

Figure 4.10: Dinosaur art from Grand Canyon courtesy of Steve Rudd. Used with permission.

Figure 4.11: Granby Idol image courtesy of Genesis Park. Used with permission.

Figure 4.12: Ankylosaurus image courtesy of Genesis Park. Used with permission.

Figure 4.13: Ica stones image courtesy of Steve Rudd. Used with permission.

Figure 4.14: Acambaro images courtesy of Steve Rudd. Used with permission.

Figure 4:15: Peru vase images courtesy of Genesis Park. Used with permission.

Figure 4.16: Behemoth chart drawn by Stephen Sebree.

Figure 4.17: Leviathan chart drawn by Stephen Sebree.

Figure 5.1: Portrait of Louis Agassiz courtesy of Wikimedia Commons / Public Domain.

Figure 5.2: Image of Archaeopteryx courtesy of James L. Amos, National Geographic Society / Wikimedia Commons / Public Domain.

Figure 5.3: Image of Sinosauropteryx courtesy of User: James St. John / Wikimedia Commons / CC BY-SA-2.0. Used with permission; usage not intended to imply endorsement by the author/licensor of the work.

Figure 5.4: Archaeoraptor fossil drawn by Stephen Sebree.

Figure 5.5: Image of Sinornithosaurus courtesy of Wikimedia Commons / Public Domain.

Figure 5.6: Alleged horse evolution chart redrawn by Stephen Sebree based on information from "Palaeontology," Encyclopædia Britannica (11th ed.), v. 20, 1911, fig. 9, 586. Public Domain.

Figure 5.7: Evolution of man drawn by Stephen Sebree.

Figure 5.8: Lucy image courtesy of User: Sapiens Ergsap / Flikr / CC BY-SA-2.0. Used with permission; usage not intended to imply endorsement by the author/licensor of the work.

Figure 5.9: Neanderthal image courtesy of User: Tim Evanson / Flikr / CC BY-SA-2.0. Used with permission; usage not intended to imply endorsement by the author/licensor of the work.

Figure 5.10: Cro Magnon image courtesy of User: 120 / Wikimedia Commons / CC BY-SA-3.0. Used with permission; usage not intended to imply endorsement by the author/licensor of the work.

Figure 5.11: Heidelberg man image courtesy of User: Tim Evanson / Flikr / CC BY-SA-2.0. Used with permission; usage not intended to imply endorsement by the author/licensor of the work.

Figure 5.12: Heidelberg jawbone image courtesy of User: Gerbil / Wikimedia Commons / CC BY-SA-2.0. Used with permission; usage not intended to imply endorsement by the author/licensor of the work.

Figure 5.13: Nebraska man courtesy of Illustrated London News (1922), via http://bevets.com/nebraska.htm / Public Domain.

Figure 5.14: Piltdown man fragments image redrawn by Stephen Sebree based on Judy Breck / Flikr / CC-BY-SA-2.0. Used with permission; usage not intended to imply endorsement by the author/licensor of the work.

Figure 6.1: Burgess shale fossils image courtesy of User: Ryan Somma / Flikr / CC BY-SA-2.0. Used with permission; usage not intended to imply endorsement by the author/licensor of the work.

Figure 6.2: Disparity precedes diversity chart drawn by Stephen Sebree.

Figure 6.3: Four-legged tank image courtesy of User: Machairo / Wikimedia Commons / CC BY-SA-4.0. Used with permission; usage not intended to imply endorsement by the author/licensor of the work.

Figure 6.4: Leonardo Image courtesy of User: The Children's Museum of Indianapolis / Wikimedia Commons / CC BY-SA-3.0. Used with permission; usage not intended to imply endorsement by the author/licensor of the work.

Figure 6.5: T-rex legbone image courtesy of Google Images. No known copyright.

Figure 6.6: Triceratops horn image courtesy of Google Images. No known copyright.

Figure 6.7: Wooly mammoth Image courtesy of User: James St. John / Wikimedia Commons / CC BY-SA-2.0. Used with permission; usage not intended to imply endorsement by the author/licensor of the work.

Figure 6.8: Fossilized hammer image courtesy of Steve Rudd. Used with permission.

Figure 6.9: Origin of Species image courtesy of Wikimedia Commons / Public Domain.

Figure 6.10: Finches image courtesy of Wikimedia Commons / Public Domain.

Figure 6.11: Peppered moth image courtesy of User: gailhampshire / Flikr / CC BY-SA-2.0. Used with permission; usage not intended to imply endorsement by the author/licensor of the work.

Figure 6.12: Great Unconformity image courtesy of User: brewbooks / Flikr / CC BY-SA-2.0. Used with permission; usage not intended to imply endorsement by the author/licensor of the work.

Figure 6.13: Grand Canyon image courtesy of User: Grand Canyon National Park / Flikr / CC BY-SA-2.0. Used with permission; usage not intended to imply endorsement by the author/licensor of the work.

Figure 6.14: Polystrate fossil image courtesy of User: Michael C. Rygel / Wikimedia Commons / CC BY-SA-3.0. Used with permission; usage not intended to imply endorsement by the author/licensor of the work.

Figure 7.1: Hand of God pulsar wind nebula image courtesy of Robert Sullivan / Flikr/ Public Domain.

Figure 7.2: Mousetrap image courtesy of Charles Rondeau / PublicDomainPictures.net / Public Domain.

Figure 7.3: Water cycle chart redrawn by Stephen Sebree based on an image from AIRS, NASA / Flikr / CC-BY-SA-2.0. Used with permission; usage not intended to imply endorsement by the author/licensor of the work.

Figure 7.4: Bacterial flagellum redrawn by Stephen Sebree based on an image from user: LadyofHats / Wikimedia Commons / Public Domain.

Figure 7.5: Human versus prosthetic hand image courtesy of Shutterstock.

Figure 7.6: Natural Theology photo courtesy of Wikimedia Commons / Public Domain.

Figure 7.7: Watch image courtesy of Shutterstock.

Figure 7.8: Nautilus image courtesy of Shutterstock.

Figure 7.9: Behe picture drawn by Stephen Sebree.

Figure 7.10: Stephen C. Meyer image courtesy of Discovery Institute / Public Domain.

Figure 8.1: Watch image courtesy of Shutterstock.

Figure 8.2: Solar system image courtesy of Shutterstock.

Figure 8.3: Moon image courtesy of Shutterstock.

Figure 8.4: Earth and moon image courtesy of Shutterstock.

Figure 8.5: Atmosphere graphic drawn by Stephen Sebree.

Figure 9.1: Human brain image courtesy of Shutterstock.

Figure 9.2: DNA diagram drawn by Stephen Sebree.

Figure 9.3: Darwin image courtesy of Wikimedia Commons / Public Domain.

Figure 9.4: Eye chart courtesy of Shutterstock.

Figure 9.5: Ear chart courtesy of Shutterstock.

Figure 9.6: Blood coagulation cascade diagram redrawn by Stephen Sebree based on information from Figure 4—3 in Behe, Darwin's Black Box, 82.
Figure 9.7: Cell diagram courtesy of User: Jake Cannon / Wikimedia Commons / CC BY-SA-3.0. Used with permission; usage not intended to imply endorsement by the author/licensor of the work.

Figure 9.8: Bad design image courtesy of User: Zyance / Wikimedia Commons / CC BY-SA-2.5. Used with permission; usage not intended to imply endorsement by the author/licensor of the work.

Figure 10.1: Information spiral diagram redrawn by Stephen Sebree based on information from Figure 33 in Gitt, In the Beginning, 191.

Figure 10.2: Amino acids chart drawn by Stephen Sebree.

Figure 10.3: Bible as communication diagram redrawn by Stephen Sebree based on information from Figure 27 in Gitt, In the Beginning, 144.

Figure 10.4: Prayer diagram redrawn by Stephen Sebree based on information from Figure 29 in Gitt, In the Beginning, 154.

Figure 11.1: Root cross-section diagram drawn by Stephen Sebree.

Figure 11.2: Ponderosa pine image courtesy of User: Brady Smith, Coconino National Forest / Wikimedia Commons / CC BY-SA-2.0. Used with permission; usage not intended to imply endorsement by the author/licensor of the work.

Figure 11.3: Lodgepole pine image courtesy of User: S. Rae / Wikimedia Commons / CC BY-SA-2.0. Used with permission; usage not intended to imply endorsement by the author/licensor of the work.

Figure 11.4: Whitebark pine image courtesy of User: Craters of the Moon National Monument and Preserve / Flikr / CC BY-SA-2.0. Used with permission; usage not intended to imply endorsement by the author/licensor of the work.

Figure 11.5: Sorghum image courtesy of User: Cyndy Sims Parrh/Flikr/CC BY-SA-2.0. Used with permission; usage not intended to imply endorsement by the author/licensor of the work.

Figure 11.6: Yucca moth image Courtesy of the National Park Service, Department of the Interior / Public Domain.

Figure 11.7: Cephalopoda image courtesy of Wikimedia Commons / Public Domain.

Figure 11.8: Lobster image courtesy of Shutterstock.

Figure 11.9: Purple sea urchins image courtesy of Shutterstock.

Figure 11.10: Bald eagle image courtesy of Shutterstock.

Figure 11.11: Bee diagram redrawn by Stephen Sebree based on information from Figure 39 in Gitt, In the Beginning, 222.

Figure 11.12: Diamond weevil image courtesy of User: Quartl / Wikimedia Commons / CC BY-SA-3.0. Used with permission; usage not intended to imply endorsement by the author/licensor of the work.

Figure 11.13: Blind cave fish (Phreatichthys andruzzi) Image courtesy of Nicola Cavallari, Elena Frigato, Daniela Vallone, Nadine Fröhlich, Jose Fernando Lopez-Olmeda, Augusto Foà, Roberto Berti, Francisco Javier Sánchez-Vázquez, Cristiano Bertolucci, Nicholas S. Foulkes/ http://journals.plos.org/plosbiology/article?id=10.1371/journal.pbio.1001142/CC BY-SA-3.0. Used with permission; usage not intended to imply endorsement by the author/licensor of the work.

Figure 11.14: Echolocation diagram redrawn by Stephen Sebree based on diagram from Marek M / Wikimedia Commons / CC-BY-SA-3.0. Used with permission; usage not intended to imply endorsement by the author/licensor of the work.

Figure 11.15: Common shrew image courtesy of Wikimedia Commons / Public Domain.

Figure 11.16: Giraffe image courtesy of User: Miroslav Duchacek / Wikimedia Commons / CC-BY-SA-3.0. Used with permission; usage not intended to imply endorsement by the author/licensor of the work.

Figure 12.1: Psalm 8 image courtesy of Shutterstock.

Figure 12.2: Irrational man image courtesy of Shutterstock.

Figure 12.3: Jacques Monod photograph courtesy of Wikimedia Commons / Public Domain.

Figure 12.4: Victor Stenger image courtesy of User: Vic Stenger / Wikimedia Commons / CC BY-SA-3.0. Used with permission; usage not intended to imply endorsement by the author/licensor of the work.

Figure 12.5: Thomas Nagel image courtesy of User: Nagelt / Wikimedia Commons / CC BY-SA-4.0. Used with permission; usage not intended to imply endorsement by the author/licensor of the work.

Figure 12.6: Julian Huxley photograph courtesy of Dutch National Archives, The Hague, Fotocollectie Algemeen Nederlands Persbureau (ANEFO), 1945-1989. Public Domain.

Figure 12.7: Michelangelo's Ezekiel in Sistine Chapel courtesy of Wikimedia Commons / Public Domain.

Figure 12.8: Michelangelo's Creation of Adam in Sistine Chapel courtesy of Shutterstock.

Made in the USA
Monee, IL
01 August 2023

40232228R00098